Jewish Art Treasures from Prague

MI28 Book cover, silver

Jewish Art Treasures from Prague

The State Jewish Museum in Prague and its collections

A catalogue compiled by the Museum in Prague
edited and with a foreword by Professor C. R. Dodwell LittD FBA

Lund Humphries, London
in association with the Whitworth Art Gallery, University of Manchester

Copyright © 1980 The Whitworth Art Gallery, Manchester

First edition 1980
Published by
Lund Humphries Publishers Ltd
26 Litchfield Street London WC2

The Whitworth Art Gallery ISBN 0 903261 16 2
Lund Humphries Publishers ISBN 0 85331 433 0 (for trade orders)

Designed by Alan Bartram
Made and printed in Great Britain by
Lund Humphries, Bradford and London

This is the catalogue of the exhibition *Jewish Art Treasures from Prague,* shown at the Whitworth
Art Gallery, University of Manchester between 7 October and 16 December 1980.
Supported by the Ministry of Culture of the Czechoslovak Socialist Republic; the Greater
Manchester Council; the British Council; the Visiting Arts Unit of Great Britain; the Granada
Foundation; the North West Arts Association; the Industrial Diamond Company Limited;
the Lord Rayne; the Heinz and Anna Kroch Foundation; Pifco Limited; Mr Cyril Stein
and Messrs J. and H. Livingstone.

Cover illustrations:
D39 Karl Fleischmann: Prisoners awaiting
deportation
T32 Cover, Bohemia: Prague (Synagogue in
Karlín), 2nd half of 19th century

Frontispiece: The Old Prague Jewish Cemetery

Contents

Foreword

The object of my visit to Czechoslovakia in 1972 was to negotiate an exchange of exhibitions between the United Kingdom and Czechoslovakia. This was later followed up by another visit in May, 1978 and, as a result, the exhibition *The Pre-Raphaelites and Related Artists* – drawn entirely from the Whitworth's own collections – was shown at the beginning of this year, first at the Slovak National Gallery in Bratislava and then at the Czech National Gallery in Prague. It was a matter of deep personal regret to me that, owing to illness, I could not attend the opening, but now, a few months later, I take the greatest pleasure in welcoming this exhibition from Czechoslovakia to the Whitworth Art Gallery. It seems to me to be unique in its combination of considerable aesthetic appeal and intense historic interest.

The collections of the State Jewish Museum in Prague, now represented for the first time in the West, constitute the greatest holding of Judaica in the world. Partly assembled by the Nazis as their monument to 'an extinct race', it was intended at one time to signify mastery and defeat, but it has the opposite connotation for us today as the State Jewish Museum triumphantly celebrates its thirtieth anniversary. For us it is a happy occasion on which to mount this historic exhibition.

It has been one of the most complex – as I believe it will be one of the most successful – of all the exhibitions that the Whitworth has organised and it could not have been accomplished without the help of a number of institutions and individuals.

I am especially indebted to Ph. Dr Miroslav Jaroš, Director of the State Jewish Museum. He and his colleagues in Prague treated me with every kindness, and allowed me to spend days selecting objects for this exhibition, at the same time giving me the benefit of their advice and scholarly appraisals. With the encouragement of his Ministry of Culture, Ph. Dr Jaroš responded to my request for loans with outstanding generosity. He and his staff then had the arduous task of preparing the following detailed introductions and catalogue for some 300 works of art for our exhibition and also making these objects ready for their journey to Manchester.

On the Czech side, the administrative work for the exhibition has been the responsibility of the Ministry of Culture of the Czechoslovak Socialist Republic and I am only too glad to acknowledge the considerable efficiency of their officers as well as the generosity of the Ministry of Culture in agreeing to bear the cost of transporting the exhibition to England and other expenses. I should also like to thank His Excellency the Czechoslovak Ambassador, Dr Zdenek Cernĭk, for kindly agreeing to open this exhibition and for the encouragement and support given by him and his staff. We are sorry that Ph. Dr Jaroš will be unable to come to the opening but we shall be delighted to welcome Ph. Dr Adolf Svoboda, Head of the Department of Culture, National Committee, Prague, and two Curators from the State Jewish Museum, Doc. PhD. Vladamír Sadek and PhD. Bedřich Nosek.

Despite all the help from Czechoslovakia, we could not have mounted an exhibition on this scale and with publicity extending abroad without extra financial help. Here, as always, we are indebted to the Greater Manchester Council, whose continuing support of our exhibitions programme is a source of great encouragement. As in the past, the

British Council have been very helpful, and I should particularly like to thank John Acton, until recently British Cultural Attaché in Prague, his successor, George Preen, and the Assistant Cultural Attaché, Miss Isobel Hunter; and, in England, Miss Margaret McLeod, of the Council's Fine Art Department and Mrs Bridget Thompson in EENAD.

Two other public institutions have given much appreciated financial help, and I should like to thank Mr Tim Scott and his successor, Mr Kenneth Pearson, at the Visiting Arts Unit and Mr Raphael Gonley of the North West Arts Association for aid from their organisations.

The list of benefactors of the exhibition does not end here, and I should like to express my warmest thanks to those individuals and organisations who have generously responded to my appeal for funds. Notable amongst these are the Granada Foundation; the Industrial Diamond Company Limited; Lord Rayne; the Heinz and Anna Kroch Foundation; Pifco Limited; Mr Cyril Stein; Messrs J. and H. Livingstone and a private fund which has asked to remain anonymous.

Mr Jack Lunzer has shown an infectious enthusiasm for the exhibition from the moment of its inception. As Library Custodian of the Valmadonna Trust, he has helped by lending some early examples of Prague Hebrew printing to the exhibition as substitutes for those in Prague which were too fragile to travel. They were selected by Professor Abramsky of University College, London. He has further very generously sponsored the visit to England of one of the Curators from Prague. I have also had great encouragement and help from the Chief Rabbi and his Executive Director, Moshe Davis; Mr Hyman Wagner and the Jewish Representative Council of Greater Manchester; Rabbi Robert Silverman; and Mr Robert Scott.

The catalogue was written by Doc. PhD. Vladamír Sadek, PhD. Bedřich Nosek, PhD. Jana Doleželová, PhD. Jana Čeramáková and Mr Arno Pařík, who have given us the benefit of their art historical scholarship and to whom we offer our particularly grateful thanks.

In editing the English version, I have had points kindly answered by Miss Carole Mendleson and Mr R. Norton of the Jewish Museum in London, Rabbi Robert Silverman of the Manchester Reform Synagogue, Dr A. Unterman, Department of Comparative Religion, University of Manchester, and the late Stuart Platts of the Manchester City Art Gallery. At Lund Humphries Publishers, John Taylor and Charlotte Burri have taken every care in seeing the catalogue through the press, and Alan Bartram has been responsible for the design work.

The exhibition within the Whitworth has been designed by Alasdair Hamilton and his colleagues in the University Audio-Visual Service, who have also styled the accompanying publicity material. The actual installation has been in the hands of Hempstead and English, aided by several voluntary assistants.

An exhibition, such as this, has called for all the resources of our own staff and I should particularly like to thank Robin Vousden for his work in arranging, co-ordinating and early publicity, all of which has been invaluable to me. The Principal

8

Keeper, Francis Hawcroft, and Vivien Knight have given considerable help. Joan Allgrove and Michael Clarke have kindly checked much detail. Mr Sargeant has contributed his technical skills. One former member of staff and one future member have generously volunteered their help and I should like to thank Michael Regan and Henny King for all they have done.

This exhibition is very much a corporate effort and I hope it will open many people's eyes to the beauties of Jewish art and to the historic circumstances which led to so much of it being assembled in Prague.

C. R. DODWELL
DIRECTOR

Dedication

The history of the Jews in Prague and in Bohemia begins in the Middle Ages. In the course of a thousand years, monuments of significance and objects of great artistic and cultural value have been made for particular Jewish communities within the regions of Bohemia and Moravia, and these are now in the care of the State Jewish Museum in Prague. Its collections originated in those of the pre-war Prague Jewish Museum but they were greatly enlarged as a result of the tragedy of World War II when most Jewish religious communities in Bohemia and Moravia became victims of the Nazi racial persecution.

This exhibition, which displays representative examples from that collection, is dedicated to the memory of those who lost their lives then.

opposite: A wall in the Pinkas Synagogue

·X 1944 RŮŽENA 31.VIII 1861·17.II 1943 · JELLINKOVÁ VINCENCIE 13.IV 1914·29.I 1943 · PRŮHONICE : SANDHOLZOVÁ MARIE 20
8.X 1942 OTTO 29.IX 1908·28.IX 1944 · LAMBERG JOSEF 20.IX 1869 RŮŽENA 4.II 1910 VĚRA 9.IV 1935·20
12.II 1891·20.II 1943 · LUSTIG ADOLF 3.IV 1852·8.XII 1942 · PICK OTO 6.VII 1899 HELENA 23.IV 1872·15.X 1942 · IL
1880 EMA 8.XI 1883·6.IX 1943 · FUCHSOVÁ ZDĚNKA 3.IX 1893·23.II 1943 · HIRSCHOVÁ REGINA 11.XI
1922·6.IX 1943 · POLLAK EDVARD 3.II 1881·6.IX 1943 OLGA 9.II 1882·25.XII 1942 · ROUBÍČEK OSKAR 14.
1895 ANNA 4.V 1899 LUDMILA 22.III 1925 JAN 16.VI 1930·23.II 1943 · SUSCHITZKÁ JANA 24.V 18
MARKÉTA 7.XII 1905·14.VII 1942 · OSKAR 9.VI 1882·14.VII 1941 · BAUMGARTEN JINDŘICH 13.II
18.XI 1904·25.VIII 1942 · DONATHOVÁ BERTA 21.VI 1883·14.VII 1942 · FELDSBERGEROVÁ RŮŽEN
VII 1934 ALICE 28.III 1936·8.X 1942 · GARTNEROVÁ JENNY 24.IV 1874·15.X 1942 · RUTH 23.III
885·25.VIII 1942 · GRŰNOVÁ JULIE 31.VII 1867·15.XII 1943 · HAAS ERICH 10.VIII 1903·28.IX 19
4.VII 1942 · OLGA 5.II 1885·8.IX 1942 · HESKÁ EVA 29.V 1932·18.V 1944 · IRMA 22.VIII 1904·26.
OMÁŠ 17.III 1938·14.VII 1942 · KLEIN OTTO 8.III 1881·1.IX 1942 · RUDOLF 3.VIII 1889 PAVLA 28.VI
HANA 28.   30 PETR 6.VII 1938·14.VII 1942 · VILÉM 21.XII 1876   GA 4.V 1891·1   1942 · MŮL
16 LEOPO   27.II 1941·15.V   44 · OLGA 3.VI   9 RUDOLF 2   III 1933·14.VII   2 · VALERIE 1
22.X 1942 F   DA 29.V 1889   NA 16.VII 1893   II 1942 · RO   NZWEIGOVÁ JINDŘIŠKA 29.
1944 · ELS   10.III 1893·14.V   1942 · SMOLINSKÝ ISIDOR 25.IV 1873·20.VII 194   DELA 12.VIII 1
IRMA   393·10.VII 1942 · ŠAMALÍKOVÁ   VÍRA 19.VI 19   14.VII 1942 · S   STNÝ ERICH
UEL 10.II   MARIE 27.II   3 JIŘÍ 14.III 1922   DOLF 13.IV 19   8.IX 1942 · TŐ   EROVÁ VIKT
1904 RUTH   II 1912 HANA   III 1936·14.VII   · WEIS VÍTĚ   LAV 19.III 1902   XII 1942 · W
WOL   CHARLOTA   V 1868·22.X 194   DĚNEK 10.VIII   20·6.IX 1943 J   2.IX 1925·28.
1194   STAVLKY :   GULAR ADOLF   1874·15.XII 19   · LUSTIGO   ANTONIE 4.
43 · H   EL 25.V 1884   LA 4.VII 1897·20.I   3 JIŘÍ 25.II 192   II 1943 HERMA   VII 1867·9.II
JOS   .VI 1943·   EIN OTTO 8.II 189   0.II 1943 ARNOŠ   A 20.II 1870·14   43 · OLGA 16
23.X   3.VII 1897·   1942 · STRICKE   VÁ ZDENKA 10   1914·20.II 1943   ·NCER OTTO
89.5   PŘÍBRA   ADLER ARNOŠT   XII 1888·1.X 1944   URT 10.II   RŮŽENA
DNIKA   .X 194   RGMANN JOSEF   894·21.VI 194   OLÍNA 5.VI 18   BI
BEDŘI   1908·8.IX 194   HERMÍNA 25.   OLÍNA   ENA 3.II   RŮŽENA 7.III 1
OLF 6.VI 19   8.IX 1942 · FRIEDHABER HERMAN 2   1909·1.III 1943   FRIEDMANN A
16.IV 19   V 19   2 · HECHT JAROSLAV 23.VII 1889 MARTHA 14.XII 1896   IX 1942 · KARE
OS M   HAO XII 19   17.VII 1929 EM   25.XII 1930 LEV   VI 1936·8.IX 1942   RICHARD 22.II
188   30·8.IX 1942 · KRAUS RUDOLF 19.VIII 1890   VII 1940 · LAVEC   REGINA 9.XI 187
13.IX 1875·19.IX 194   3 · MÜLLER B   IN 13.III 186   VILMA
CNOVÁ ANNA 24.V 1892   1929·16.X 1944 · P   K RICHARD   DA 18.X
DĚNKA 5.IX 1894 HANA 7.V 1929·16.X 1944   1879 EMIL 15.II   X 1942 · SCHA
ROSENZW   021.III 1880 HEDVI   9.8.IX 1942   INOVÁ KAROLI
8.I   42 ·   MARTA 18.IV 1894 HANA   1882 KAM   83·8.IX 1942 · TURN
1942   A 4.VI 1914·8.X 1942   2 · TŐPFER ARTUR   WEINEROVÁ   11875·15.X 1942 · REINIG
190   DĚNKA 2   23.X 1890·8.IX 19   .IV 1921 EGON 8   25.V 1942 · WEISSENS
883 ALŽBĚ   23.X 1915 JU   ELEONORA 2.V   4 ALOIS 2.IV 1868·24.VII 1942
912 MILAN 2   .IX 19   VLASTA 2.IX 1904·28   FELIX 8.X 1924·20.II 1943 · WILL
15.X 1942   RNÝ P   JINDŘ   SOŇA 4.IX 1928·23.II 1943 ·
KIESL   HUMIL 5.   1896 JINDŘ   OTA 1.IX 1912·25.V 1942 ·
R BEDŘICH 12.V 1883   18.II 1899 E   PUSTÁ RYBNÁ : FU
1886 HEDVI   1879·22.IX 1942 · MARIE 24.VIII 1912·17.III 1942 ·
STEIN A   REINISCH ALBERT 26.I

The pre-war exhibition

Historical introduction

The Prague Jewish Museum in the Pre-War Period

The Association for Establishing a Jewish Museum in Prague was founded in 1906 at the instance of S. H. Lieben (a scientist from Prague, 1881–1942). It began by collecting objects of artistic value from synagogues and elsewhere, and in 1909 parts of its collections were made accessible to the public. In 1912 the collections were placed in the building of the Prague Burial Brotherhood (*Ḥevra Kadisha*) and, in 1926, the Prague Jewish Museum was given the building of the Ceremonial Hall (the mortuary) at the entrance to the Old Prague Jewish Cemetery. Here the Prague Jewish Museum was domiciled until the beginning of World War II. At that time its inventory listed about one thousand exhibits.

The Prague Jewish Museum during World War II

After the occupation of Bohemia and Moravia, the Nazis introduced their anti-Jewish 'Nuremberg Laws' into the so-called Protectorate. Those who were Jews, or of Jewish origin, were separated by force from the other inhabitants and deported to a concentration camp, established in the town of Terezín, North Bohemia, which was called 'Ghetto Theresienstadt' and later on 'Jüdisches Siedlungsgebiet'. Almost all of the inhabitants were subsequently murdered in extermination camps. A great number of Jews (about 35,000 people) perished in Terezín itself.

The deportations to Terezín began in November 1941 and, in March 1942, the Nazis dissolved all Jewish religious communities in Bohemia and Moravia. Art objects, books, archive material and other objects owned by Jewish religious communities, synagogues and individuals were then ordered to be gathered in Prague, where in August 1942 the so-called Central Jewish Museum ('Jüdisches Zentral Museum Prag') was established.

The Setting-up of the 'Central Jewish Museum'

The so-called 'Central Jewish Museum in Prague' was not a museum in the usual sense of the word. The Nazis simply planned it as a place where objects confiscated from synagogues and elsewhere should be deposited and professionally studied. In accordance with Nazi ideology, it was to serve as a museum of 'an extinct race'. At the same time, the most valuable objects were selected and exhibited in Prague synagogues. The exhibitions were not accessible to the public and only some Nazis could visit them.

Work in the 'Central Jewish Museum'

The study of art-historical objects, books and archive material was made by groups of Jewish experts in the fields of Hebrew studies, history, history of art and museology. Their aims were quite different from those of the Nazis. They endeavoured to save the valuable artistic and cultural objects of the Jews in Bohemia and Moravia, and the internal exhibitions were designed in a scholarly and objective spirit in sharp contradiction to the Nazi ideology. Though in direct conflict with the Nazis who actually controlled the museum, they were the real creators of the war-time Jewish Museum in Prague. Their work can be seen as a kind of spiritual combat against the Nazis by whom most of them were ultimately murdered: Dr Josef Polák (before the war an expert in the field of museology and the Director of the museum in Kosice) perished in prison on 7 November 1944; the architect Frantisek Zelenka (a well-known playwright) perished in Auschwitz, to which he was deported on 28 September 1944; Dr Tobias Jakobovits (librarian of the Prague Jewish Religious Community) perished in Auschwitz, to which he was deported on 27 October 1944; Professor Dr Alfred Engel (founder of the Jewish Museum at Mikulov in Moravia) perished in Terezín on 9 June 1944.

Before they died, these men, together with others, formed a legacy which inspired the workers of the post-war Prague Jewish Museum. They studied most of the objects that had been collected, and they also set up several exhibitions: for example, one of old Hebrew printed books and manuscripts in the High Synagogue, another of Jewish festivals and customs in the Klausen Synagogue, and a third presenting the development of the Prague ghetto which was shown in the building of the pre-war Jewish Museum.

The Establishment of the State Jewish Museum in Prague

After Prague was liberated in May 1945, the artistic and cultural objects assembled in the Prague Jewish Museum remained as a tragic witness to the fate of the majority of Jewish religious communities in Bohemia and Moravia during the Nazi occupation.

As early as June 1946, some of the exhibitions that had been prepared during World War II were made accessible to the public and, in order that these treasures should be preserved for future generations, the Czechoslovak State, in agreement with the Council of Jewish Religious Communities in Bohemia and Moravia, assumed responsibility for their care.

The State Jewish Museum in Prague was established on 4 April 1950.

Transportation from Terezín

Transportation from Terezín

Classifying of textiles

Chandeliers stored in a synagogue

The State Jewish Museum in Prague, its collections and the main fields of its activities

Historic Monuments

The basic concern of the State Jewish Museum in Prague is with the material and spiritual legacy of the Jewish communities in Bohemia and Moravia, their study in terms of scholarship and museology, their accessibility to the general public in the form of exhibitions, and their scholarly publication.

The Museum's exhibitions and permanent displays are set in the historic buildings of the synagogues of Prague – in the Maisel, Klausen, High and Spanish Synagogues, and in the Ceremonial Hall at the Old Prague Jewish Cemetery. The care of these exceptionally valuable historical monuments, which were once part of the Old Prague Jewish Town, is now understandably one of the basic activities of the Museum. Care is also devoted to the restoration of objects in the collection, especially those from synagogues. These include objects in silver, textiles and pictures.

The *Alt-Neu Synagogue* is the most significant building of the Old Prague Jewish Town. It was built in the last third of the thirteenth century in the Cistercian Gothic style. Its brick gables date back to the fifteenth century and the women's galleries were added in the seventeenth and eighteenth centuries. The Alt-Neu Synagogue is owned by the Prague Jewish Religious Community and is used for regular Jewish religious services together with another Prague synagogue in the Jeruzalémská Street.

Within the area of the *Old Prague Jewish Cemetery* there are about 12,000 tombstones. The oldest, that of the poet and scholar Avigdor Kara, dates back to the year 1439. The last funeral took place there in 1787. A number of personalities who played a part in the history of the Jews are buried in the cemetery. They include the philosopher, scholar and teacher, Yehuda Lev ben Betzsalel (Rabbi Löw) who died in 1609 and who, according to legend, was the creator of an artificial being called 'the Golem'. The cemetery is also the last resting place of the historian and astronomer, David Gans (1541–1613), of the Mayor of the Prague Jewish Town, Mordecai Maisel (1528–1601), of the scientist and philospher, Joseph Solomon Delmedigo (1591–1655), of the scholar and bibliophile, David Oppenheim (1664–1736), whose collection of books and manuscripts is now in the Bodleian Library, Oxford, and of a number of others. The cultural and historical interest of the tombstones is supplemented by their artistic qualities. A number are decorated with reliefs depicting the occupations of the dead, symbolising their names, or perhaps expressing their membership of families of priests – the Cohens or the Levites. There are a number of carved figures (for example, those of the deceased maidens) and these are quite rare in other Jewish cemeteries in Bohemia and Moravia. Systematic restoration and conservation of the tombstones has been undertaken in recent years. This work is organised by the State Jewish Museum in co-operation with the State Institute for the Care of Monuments in Prague.

The *Maisel Synagogue* was founded by the Mayor of the Prague Jewish Town, Mordecai Maisel. Its builders were Juda Coref (Goldschmied) de Herz and Joseph Wahl. The original Renaissance building was destroyed by the fire of 1689 in the Prague Jewish Town. It was replaced by an early Baroque synagogue in 1691, and finally it was rebuilt in 1894 in the Neo-Gothic style. Today the Maisel Synagogue has

The exhibition in the former Ceremonial Hall

The Alt–Neu Synagogue in Maisel Street

a permanent exhibition of 'Silver Objects from Czech Synagogues' and also contains part of the Museum's holdings.

The *Pinkas Synagogue* originally belonged to the Horowitz family from Prague. It was formerly part of a private house owned by this family, but was rebuilt in the first half of the sixteenth and again at the beginning of the seventeenth century to give more of its present-day appearance. In the 1860s and in the year 1950 it received further modifications. After World War II, in 1954–9, a Memorial to the Victims of Nazism from Bohemia and Moravia, who perished as a result of Nazi racial persecution, was set up in the Pinkas Synagogue. The names of the victims were inscribed on the walls of the interior and included their principal dates (the dates of their births, of their deportations to the concentration camp of Terezín, of their deaths in Terezín, or of their departure from Terezín for Nazi extermination camps). This deeply poignant Memorial provides us with a vivid picture of the extent of Nazi crimes.

Unfortunately, it was discovered that the inscriptions on the walls were gradually, but seriously, being damaged by damp and underground water. This necessitated the closure of the Memorial for repairs which will be finished within the next two years. For a number of technical reasons, these will change its general appearance though, when the Memorial is made accessible to the public, it will again be in its original form incorporating the names of the victims of Nazism. It is then hoped to make accessible other features (such as the medieval Jewish ritual bath, *mikveh*) which were discovered underground during the restoration of the synagogue.

The *High Synagogue* came into existence about the second half of the sixteenth century. The building was financed by Mordecai Maisel, and the architect was the Italian master-builder Pankrac Roder. The hall of the High Synagogue with its Renaissance plaster vault is on the first floor, which explains why the High Synagogue is so called. Some time ago the interior was restored, and at present a new exhibition of synagogue textiles is being prepared for it.

Like the Pinkas Synagogue, the *Klausen Synagogue* is in close proximity to the Old Prague Jewish Cemetery. It, too, was founded by Mordecai Maisel. Originally three smaller buildings called 'klauses' stood there. One of them contained the *yeshiva* (the Talmudic school) where Rabbi Löw used to teach. The present-day synagogue was built after the fire in the Prague Jewish Town of 1689. In 1883–4 it was extended and in 1910 partially rebuilt. At present the interior of the Klausen Synagogue is being restored to receive an exhibition of old Hebrew printed books and manuscripts illustrating the development of Hebrew literature in Bohemia and Moravia from the Middle Ages to the first half of the nineteenth century.

The *Spanish Synagogue* is situated in that part of the old Jewish settlement in Prague, where a synagogue called the 'Old School' originally stood. The present building was erected during the second half of the nineteenth century in a pseudo-Moorish style, with its internal decoration following that of the Spanish Alhambra. An exhibition of the art of synagogue textiles is displayed inside. The entrance hall of the synagogue and the hall on the first floor are used for temporary museum exhibitions.

The former *Ceremonial Hall of the Prague Burial Brotherhood,* built at the beginning of the twentieth century in a pseudo-Romanesque style, is the newest building within the compass of the State Jewish Museum. Today it houses an exhibition of children's drawings and poems from the concentration camp of Terezín which was first opened in 1979 on the occasion of the International Year of the·Child.

Material from the Terezín Concentration Camp
CHILDREN'S ART (DI–D38)
A considerable portion of the material and collections of the State Jewish Museum is related to the concentration camp of Terezín, which was established by the Nazis at the end of 1941.

The Terezín prisoners included thousands of children who – with only a few exceptions – were murdered by the Nazis in the gas-chambers of the extermination camps. However, the children's drawings and writings were preserved. They were made during lessons which were organised by educationalists imprisoned in Terezín. About 5,000 drawings have survived. They illustrate the memories and unfulfilled dreams of these child artists – the simple depiction of their lost homes, of children playing, of children's toys, of dishes full of food. Even under the cruel conditions of the concentration camp, fairy-tale motifs and childish fantasies developed, though the most tragic part of the whole collection is the drawings of Terezín itself in all its stark reality – its buildings, its crowded barracks, the distribution of food, the sick, the guards, the deportations, the funerals and the executions.

The signatures on the drawings, the dates of birth, and of deportation to Terezín, and from Terezín to the Nazi extermination camps – this is all that is generally known of the lot of these children who, in their drawings, have left us heart-rending evidence of the brutality of Fascism and war.

ADULT ARTISTS (D39–D61)
Apart from children's drawings, a number of works of art by mature artists, imprisoned in the concentration camp of Terezín during World War II, are preserved. Their creations attempt to depict the real face of Terezín – a stop on the way to death. Made with limited technical means during the evenings and at night, these hundreds of drawings depict the fate of the prisoners from their arrival in Terezín to their deportation to the Nazi extermination camps. They are now among the collections of the State Jewish Museum in Prague or among the collections of the Terezín Memorial. With the sole exception of Professor Leo Haas (who now lives in the German Democratic Republic), their authors perished in Terezín, Auschwitz or in other Nazi extermination camps.

Interior of the Alt-Neu Synagogue

Aron ha-kodesh in the Alt–Neu Synagogue

Synagogue Textiles (T1–T41)

The textile collection of the State Jewish Museum in Prague represents an exceptionally valuable holding of woven and embroidered items, dating from the late Renaissance to the twentieth century. They mostly derive from the Jewish religious communities of the Czech lands.

The collection contains about 10,000 pieces – mostly synagogue curtains, Torah mantles, draperies, pelmets, pulpit coverings, etc. As well as richly embroidered and expensive materials imported from abroad, home-made pieces, produced from materials in common production and in techniques known to most households, are also to be found. This gives these textiles significance not only for the study of the arts of the synagogue but also for the study of textile production, techniques and trade within Bohemia and Moravia.

CURTAINS AND PELMETS

The most costly textile of the synagogue is the curtain (*parochet*), a monumental screen covering the Ark (*Aron ha-kodesh*), where the parchment scrolls of the Torah (the Five Books of Moses) are placed. Above the curtain is a pelmet – a narrow strip of cloth, often cut out at the bottom. The basic scheme for the decoration of the curtains was usually one with columns on both sides. The Hebrew dedication is generally found at the top and a strip of expensive cloth or embroidery is placed in the middle. This scheme, imitating the architecture of the Ark, remained the same for centuries. In the course of the nineteenth century it was simplified as a result of the influence of folk art. The oldest curtain from the collections of the State Jewish Museum is the one presented to the Alt-Neu Synagogue in Prague by Solomon Gold in 1592. The oldest piece of cloth dates back to 1480 and was re-used in a curtain made for the Pinkas Synagogue in Prague in 1638.

MANTLES

The Torah mantle is used to cover the parchment scroll of the Torah. The basis of its decoration is the column scheme as in the case of the curtains. As well as symbols also to be found on the curtains, e.g. lions, seven-branched candelabra, Levite sets (lavers and ewers), tables with unleavened bread, the tables of the Decalogue or three crowns, they can have in addition motifs of the blessing hands (the Cohen or priestly symbol) or the Star (or Shield) of David, accompanied by the Hebrew letters *Kav Tav* (*Keter Tora* – Torah crown). The oldest Torah mantles in the collections of the State Jewish Museum go back to the sixteenth and seventeenth centuries, for example the mantle given to the Maisel Synagogue by its founder Mordecai Maisel, which is dated 1592.

SMALLER TEXTILES

Smaller textiles, which were used during various festive occasions such as the birth of a child and personal anniversaries, have their own interest and significance. They can be divided into two artistic groups: those embodying typical folklore elements and those

The tomb of David Oppenheim

of a more or less urban character. Those of a folklore character are embroidered on white linen in light colours, varying from light pink and other soft shades to red and blue. The embroidery technique is simple. In most cases cotton thread without any underlay is used for chain and cord stitches. The embroidered decoration is either plant-like or geometrical and it is often an intrinsic part of the Hebrew dedication. We find this mostly on the covers made on the occasion of the birth of a child or on those used during the festivals of *Pesaḥ* (Passover) and Sabbath in the home.

The covers of an urban character use materials such as velvet, silk, embroidery on canvas and sometimes even linen. More colours appear in the embroidery, including green and yellow. The plant and animal decoration is worked in cord and covering stitches, and reflects the influences of its own period.

WRAPPERS

The collection of wrappers, made for the birth of a son and for the binding of the Torah scroll, is unique. Some come from regions celebrated for their embroidery, such as Southern and Western Bohemia and Southern Moravia, where the original ornament was enriched with motifs from local folklore.

Some of the wrappers bear comparison with the urban-type covers both from the point of view of material and of embroidery, though the actual workmanship is more exacting. They mostly date from the eighteenth and nineteenth centuries. Apart from animal and plant motifs they can incorporate scenes with figures, such as the depiction of a wedding, or of a marriage canopy (*Ḥuppah*), etc.

Silver and other Metalwork from the Synagogues (MI–MI62)

The collection of silver objects, used in synagogues or at divine services in private households, is another significant art-historical feature of the Museum's holdings. Several go back to the sixteenth century, but most belong to the eighteenth and nineteenth centuries. They were mainly made in workshops in Bohemia, Moravia or Vienna, where the orders from various Jewish religious communities in the Czech lands were discharged. Some pieces were also made in the workshop of the Prague Jewish Goldsmiths' Guild, which existed in the Prague Jewish Town in the first half of the nineteenth century.

SILVER DECORATION OF THE TORAH SCROLLS

The heart of the collection consists of the silver adornments used to decorate the parchment scrolls of the Torah when it was used during services in the synagogue. The wooden rods, on which the scrolls are wound, are decorated with silver finials. The Torah, covered with a mantle, is also hung with a silver breastplate and with a pointer in the form of a hand, which is used in the reading of the Hebrew Biblical text. The decoration of the Torah is often completed by a silver crown at its top, as an alternative to the finials.

Jewish
Art Treasures
from Prague

Whitworth Art Gallery
7th October – 16th December 1980

Jewish Art Treasures from Prague

A major exhibition of Jewish art treasures, never previously seen in the West, goes on show at the Whitworth Art Gallery, Manchester from 7th October, 1980. It is of great historic importance, spanning Jewish culture from the 16th century onwards, and of tragic significance, since most of it was assembled by the Nazis as their record of an 'extinct race'. The exhibition will be shown only in Manchester and includes almost three hundred magnificent examples of historic Jewish art, amongst them:-

Silver and Metalwork
Silver, silver-gilt and jewelled crowns, silver breastplates and finials made to decorate the scrolls of the Torah, spice boxes in delicate silver filigree, candelabra, ewers, dishes and plates.

Synagogue Textiles
Elaborately decorated pelmets and curtains made for the Ark, gold and silver embroidered velvet mantles for the Torah, wrappers and covers.

The Prague Burial Brotherhood
A unique cycle of 18th century paintings showing the ritual of the Prague Burial Brotherhood, miniature portraits of the Brothers and glass, ceramics and silver utensils used by them.

Terezin Drawings
Original drawings from the concentration camp at Terezin include a number by some of the 15000 children who passed through the camp between 1942 and 1944, as well as examples by adult artists.

The State Jewish Museum
The history of Prague's Jewish Museum is told with documents and photographs showing its modest origins at the beginning of the century, its transformation under the Nazis into one of the world's greatest collections of Judaica, and its present day activities as it celebrates the thirtieth anniversary of its foundation under the Czechoslovak State in 1950.

Jewish Art Treasures from Prague
Open 10 am – 5 pm except Sundays with an evening extension till 9 pm on Thursdays. Admission is free. For further information, please contact the Exhibitions Officer, Whitworth Art Gallery, University of Manchester, Manchester M15 6ER. Telephone: 061-273 4865.

Shown under the auspices of the Ministry of Culture of the Czechoslovak Socialist Republic. Supported by the Greater Manchester Council, the Visiting Arts Unit, the Granada Foundation, the British Council, North West Arts Association and a number of private sponsors.

The ceiling in the High Synagogue

Aron ha-kodesh in the High Synagogue

Interior of the Maisel Synagogue

SPICE BOXES

The collection of spice boxes, used in the home during the festivals which end the Sabbath, is a significant feature of the other holdings. In artistic terms, they are mostly in a filigree technique and in turret form, but there are also spice boxes in the form of fruit, flowers, fish and, in the nineteenth century, even in the form of ships, engines, etc.

LEVITE SETS

Levite sets, the lavers and ewers used for the symbolic washing of hands during the ceremonies of the synagogue, are also included in the exhibits.

SMALLER SILVER OBJECTS

The collection of silver objects is completed by circumcision sets, a filigree cover for the prayer book, a filigree case for the scroll of the Book of Esther, dishes for citrus fruits, cups, and goblets.

CANDELABRA

Like the Sabbath lamps, the candelabra are mostly made of brass and they were obviously imported into Bohemia from Eastern Europe, probably from Poland. Eight-branched Ḥanukah candlesticks and Ḥanukah lamps of the bench type are the most frequent. They are used on the occasion of the Ḥanukah festival (the feast of dedication, commonly called the Feast of Lights) as a reminder of the reconsecration of the Temple in Jerusalem during the revolt of the Maccabees.

PEWTER PLATES

The collection of pewter plates is a remarkable one. It can be divided into two groups. The first group was used during the *Pesaḥ* (Passover) feast called Seder. The Seder plates are decorated with engraved inscriptions, and with traditional symbols or illustrations which relate to the texts of the *Pesaḥ Haggadah* (i.e. Passover narration) read during the ceremony. The second consists of wedding plates – presents for the bridegroom. Many of them take over ornamental motifs common in Czech and Moravian folk art, as we also find with Bohemian and Moravian covers for the Torah and other Jewish manuscripts of the eighteenth and nineteenth centuries.

The former Ceremonial Hall (mortuary)

Interior of the Spanish Synagogue

Early Printed Books and Manuscripts

The State Jewish Museum also has a large library specialising in Hebrew and Jewish studies. Its earliest holdings were legacies from Jewish scholars, such as Solomon Yehuda Rapaport (1790–1867), one of the founders of modern Jewish studies.

EARLY HEBREW BOOKS PRINTED AT PRAGUE

The collection of Hebrew printed books from Old Prague is the most valuable single holding of the library. Those published in the sixteenth and seventeenth centuries by the Prague Hebrew printing house of the Gersonides family are among the most remarkable examples of the Hebrew art of printing. The oldest of these books in the State Jewish Museum is a unique book of benedictions (grace before meals) – *Birkat ha-mazon,* published in Prague in 1514. The book is decorated with a number of woodcuts similar to those of the second edition of the Pentateuch published in 1530.

Some of the eighteenth-century Prague Hebrew publications, decorated with folk-art woodcuts, are also quite remarkable. They relate to the texts of the Passover *Haggadah* or to Jewish festivals and customs.

HEBREW MANUSCRIPTS

The collections also include Hebrew manuscripts. Several of them date back to the Middle Ages (e.g. the manuscript of festival prayers, the so-called *Mahzor,* of 1347), but most belong to the eighteenth and nineteenth centuries. The illustrated manuscripts from the eighteenth and the beginning of the nineteenth centuries are the most interesting. They were written by authors from various Jewish religious communities in Bohemia and Moravia. The most remarkable, which contains circumcision prayers` and rules, was that produced in 1728 by Aharon ben Benjamin from Jevicko. There is also an important manuscript of the *Haggadah* written by Natan ben Shimshon from Mezirici in 1729.

Book of benedictions (*Birkat ha-mazon*)
Prague 1514

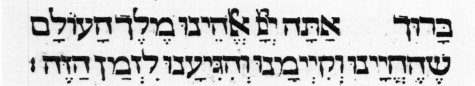

 בָּרוּךְ אַתָּה יְיָ אֱלֹהֵינוּ מֶלֶךְ הָעוֹלָם
שֶׁהֶחֱיָנוּ וְקִיְּמָנוּ וְהִגִּיעָנוּ לִזְמַן הַזֶּה ׃

צורת הציד צודה הַיוֹרנבת עם כלבו ·   והיוחר תופשו בעקבין ·
והיין צועקת במר נפש מנוחה הדריכוני   מון עקבי יסבוני ·

בשחל שבועות במוצאי שבת מתחיל כאן

בָּרוּךְ אַתָּה יְיָ אֱלֹהֵינוּ מֶלֶךְ
הָעוֹלָם בּוֹרֵא פְּרִי הַגָּפֶן ׃
בָּרוּךְ אַתָּה יְיָ אֱלֹהֵינוּ מֶלֶךְ
הָעוֹלָם אֲשֶׁר בָּחַר בָּנוּ

וַחֲמִשָּׁה:

בריך דיהנתן

לגאלי

והוידיש

כירון ראשה

Haggadah, Prague 1763

Book of benedictions (*Birkat ha-mazon*), Prague 1763

אבינו מלכנו   עשה למען ההרוגיעל ׳

אבינו מלכנו   עשה למען רחמיך הרבים ׳

אבינו מלכנו   עשה למען שמך הגדול הגבור והבורא שנקרא עלינ׳

אבינו מלכנו   חננו ועננו כי אין בנו מעשים עשה

עמנו צדקה וחסד והושיענו ״

קדיש

למוסף   מתפללין   ״

ברוך אתה יי אלהינו ואלהי אבותינו אלהי אברהם אלהי יצחק
ואלהי יעקב האל הגדול הגיבור והנורא אל עליון גומל
חסדים טובים וקונה הכל ויוכר חסדי אבות ו מוסר חכמי
ונבונים ומלמד דעת מבינים אפתחה פי בתפילה התחתונים
להודות ולהלל בני מלך מנוחל סודות מגל

ונענה סיומה שרים יחד לצרימה ״

נעה מיטר יסודותיה   בטחון בחזק מוסדותיה

בם תקעה יתדותיה   בכפל להשעין יהודתיה

המוכה בפעל צורים   הומיה המה היוצרים

עמיק ה
אדיפה
שבת
שבהון
לקיימה
שורש

וְאָתָא תּוֹרָא וְשָׁתָא לְמַיָּא דְּכָבָא לְנוּרָא דְּשָׂרַף
לְחוּטְרָא דְּהִכָּה לְכַלְבָּא דְּנָשַׁךְ
לְשׁוּנְרָא דְּאָכְלָה לְגַדְיָא דְּזַבִּין
אַבָּא בִּתְרֵי זוּזֵי חַד גַּדְיָא
חַד גַּדְיָא ׃

וְאָתָא הַשּׁוֹחֵט וְשָׁחַט
לְתוֹרָא דְּשָׁתָא
לְמַיָּא דְּכָבָא לְנוּרָא דְּשָׂרַף
לְחוּטְרָא דְּהִכָּה לְכַלְבָּא דְּנָשַׁךְ
לְשׁוּנְרָא דְּאָכְלָה לְגַדְיָא דְּזַבִּין
אַבָּא בִּתְרֵי זוּזֵי חַד גַּדְיָא ·
חַד גַּדְיָא ׃

וְאָתָא מַלְאַךְ הַמָּוֶת וְשָׁחַט
לְשׁוֹחֵט דְּשָׁחַט
לְתוֹרָא דְּשָׁתָא לְמַיָּא דְּכָבָא
לְנוּרָא דְּשָׂרַף לְחוּטְרָא דְּהִכָּה
לְכַלְבָּא דְּנָשַׁךְ לְשׁוּנְרָא דְּאָכְלָה
לְגַדְיָא דְּזַבִּין אַבָּא בִּתְרֵי זוּזֵי
חַד גַּדְיָא · חַד גַּדְיָא ׃

וְאָתָא הַקָּדוֹשׁ בָּרוּךְ הוּא
וְשָׁחַט לְמַלְאַךְ הַמָּוֶת
דְּשָׁחַט לְשׁוֹחֵט דְּשָׁחַט לְתוֹרָא
דְּשָׁתָא לְמַיָּא דְּכָבָא לְנוּרָא דְּשָׂרַף לְחוּטְרָא
דְּהִכָּה לְכַלְבָּא דְּנָשַׁךְ לְשׁוּנְרָא · דְּאָכְלָה
לְגַדְיָא · דְּזַבִּין אַבָּא בִּתְרֵי זוּזֵי · חַד גַּדְיָא ·
חַד גַּדְיָא ׃

תַּם וְנִשְׁלַם שֶׁבַח לְאֵל בּוֹרֵא
עוֹלָם

Material Relating to the Prague Burial Brotherhood

The Association of the Burial Brotherhood (*Ḥevra Kadisha*) was founded in Prague in the second half of the sixteenth century and Rabbi Löw himself helped to work out its statutes. The main activities of the Prague Burial Brotherhood included taking care of the sick and the dying. They were also in charge of funerals, of the care of cemeteries and of charities, such as infirmaries, hospitals, etc.

PICTURES (P1–P23)

A cycle of pictures made at the end of the eighteenth century by an unknown artist represents the activities of the Association. The members of the managing committee of the Prague Burial Brotherhood in the year 1773 are also portrayed in eight contemporary miniatures.

CERAMICS (M121, M122)

Unique among the exhibits are glass or earthenware jugs and mugs, painted with scenes representing the activities of the Burial Brotherhood. The jugs were used at annual meetings, when the new managing committee was elected and new members were admitted. After the meetings there were feasts given by the new members of the committee.

SMALLER OBJECTS

The Burial Brotherhood also owned some silver objects – charity boxes, ballot-boxes, plates for gifts of charity, combs, cleaners, among others.

Conclusion

The year in which this exhibition is held at the Whitworth Art Gallery is the thirtieth anniversary of the State Jewish Museum in Prague. Today it employs more than 40 specialists, including a number of experts in the fields of Hebrew and Jewish studies, of history, of the history of art, of museology and of silver and textile restoration.

Apart from systematically studying the extensive collections and making them accessible to the public in the form of exhibitions, the museum also pursues academic work in the fields of Hebrew and Jewish studies and art history. The results of this work are published bi-annually in the Museum's Journal, *Judaica Bohemiae,* and guidebooks and catalogues are produced as well. On average, the Museum receives about 750,000 visitors each year. The Museum is financed by the State, which in this way helps to develop a broad range of museum and academic activities. All this testifies to the care which the Czechoslovak Socialist Republic takes of historical, cultural and artistic monuments and relics. Among these, the Old Prague Jewish Town and the rich museum collections, reflecting a thousand years of historical, cultural and artistic development of the Jewish inhabitants of the Czech lands, are of special significance.

16 Curtain, Bohemia:
Prague
(Alt–Neu Synagogue),
1687

II
17 Curtain, Bohemia: Prague
(Pinkas Synagogue), 1869

III
110 Curtain, Bohemia:
Mladá Boleslav, 1702

IV, a
T18 Mantle, Bohemia: Prague (Pinkas Synagogue), 1671

IV, b
T24 Mantle, Bohemia: Nový Bydžov, 1765

T22 Mantle, Bohemia: Bydžov, 1743

VI
M107 Silver dish, c.1850

VII
M31 Crown, silver, parcel-gilt, 1913

VIII, a
M122 Mug of *Ḥevra Kadisha*, Bohemian glass, 1783/4

VIII, b
M121 Jug of *Ḥevra Kadisha*, pottery, 1836

Catalogue

Notes to the Catalogue

* after title denotes the exhibit is illustrated in
black and white in the catalogue.

Measurements are given in centimetres, height
before width.

Inscriptions, where given, are in translation.

Numbers at the end of catalogue entries denote
inventory numbers of the State Jewish
Museum collections.

† in drawings section denotes the artist died in
the concentration camps; and deportation
dates refer to deportation to Terezín and
deportation thereafter to the extermination
camps.

Children's drawings from the Terezín Concentration Camp

The 15,000 children who passed through the Terezín concentration camp and who mostly died in the extermination camp of Auschwitz in the autumn of 1944 are chiefly commemorated by the 5,000 drawings they left. These were found at Terezín after the war when searches were made to document the Nazi persecution. The drawings are today among the collections of the State Jewish Museum.

Illegal lessons were organised for the older boys and girls at Terezín. Of special importance among these were the art classes arranged by an artist and teacher, Mrs Friedel Dicker-Brandejsová (died 1944 in Auschwitz). For short periods, handicraft classes were officially permitted. These could be organised on a more regular basis and were of help in stimulating the interest of children of different ages, religions and nationalities. Mrs Brandejsová was interested in the psychology of children's art and tried to use her classes as a gentle educational force. Helped to self-realisation by art, the children were enabled to express their dreams and their individual ideas. This was something new and of great importance for children in the depressing atmosphere of a concentration camp. Though drawings were made earlier, those that are preserved are mainly from 1943 and the first half of 1944. They are mostly signed, which means that it is often possible to identify drawings from different occasions and with different subjects by the same artist.

There was a serious shortage of equipment and material in the camp so the classes made use of anything available at the moment. Perhaps this explains why there is such a variety of media in the collection. Children drew with pencils, crayons, charcoal or watercolours, on old technical drawings, on printed forms, on poor-quality paper or on blotting-paper of different sizes and shapes.

From an artistic point of view, the most interesting are the collages made of coloured paper with textiles and other materials. This technique enabled the children's imagination to develop freely.

There are two main themes in the children's drawings. The first relates to memories of home and of the happy moments of childhood, to the world of nature and of fairy-tales. This was the world from which the children had been shut out for years. Yet the awakening of their memories in these drawings shows the strength of their imagination. The second reflects aspects of life in the concentration camp – continual insecurity, disease, shortage of food, lack of hygiene and the death of close relatives. Coping through art with these grim facts could, with the aid of teachers, help the children to find a certain steadfastness and enable them to cling on to their own personalities.

The children's nostalgic fantasies evoked images of home – parents, brothers, sisters, flowers at the window, family reunions at supper, houses and gardens. Again and again the children recalled trips and holidays. A path through the countryside displaying signs showing the way to Prague or Brno tells much about their homesickness. Children's games were often depicted; also skiing in winter, dancing in meadows, country fairs, kiosks selling sweets. The world of fairy-tales with charmed princesses and gingerbread houses was also brought to life. Other drawings show the beauties of

D2 Nelly Silvínová: Girl standing in a flowery
meadow

nature – meadows densely covered with flowers, green vegetation, butterflies flying in blue skies, woods and trees in bloom.

The second group, representing the concentration–camp environment, is not a simple record of reality, but an expression of the emotions and attitudes towards it. The drawings of enclosed yards, of cheerless barracks, impenetrable walls, closed gates, bare windows, leafless trees in parks, of the town in black silhouette and of the sheer hills behind the town, reveal the children's environment as they saw it. Whether made in class or outside, the drawings express the children's inner feelings and fears. This is especially true of a small group of drawings depicting particular events in the camp: a funeral, an execution, an arrest, the distribution of food, the arrival of a new transport. Such subjects go beyond any normal limits of the child's world and provide the most shocking evidence of the life of the children at Terezín.

D3 Unidentified: The sun appearing behind hills

D5 Hana Wagnerová: Six girls holding hands
in a summer meadow

D11 Erika Taussigová: A vase of flowers and
other sketches

Hana Grünfeld. VI 1944 48

UNIDENTIFIED
D1 Cat, dog and other animals
pastel on reverse of green paper: 20×24.5
Inscribed *XIII*.
121.501

† NELLY SILVÍNOVÁ, born 21 December 1931;
deported 10 August 1942 and 4 October 1944.
D2 Girl standing in a flowery meadow*
pastel on thin yellowish paper: 17.5×25
Inscribed *Nelly Silvin,* and on the reverse:
Nelly Silvínová V. and *IX/13/7*.
121.563

UNIDENTIFIED
D3 The sun appearing behind hills*
pastel on irregularly shaped paper: 21×25.5
Inscribed *Renka*.
121.647

† IRENA KARPELESOVÁ, born 30 December 1930;
deported 22 December 1942 and 23 October
1944.
**D4 Autumn scene with goats and
goat-herd**
watercolour on yellowish paper: 20.5×30.5
Inscribed *Karpeles Irena*.
121.662

† HANKA WAGNEROVÁ, born 19 September
1933;
deported 24 April 1942 and 6 October 1944.
**D5 Six girls holding hands in a summer
meadow***
pencil and pastel on greyish paper: 22×31
Inscribed *Hanka Wagnerová II – group 12 N.*
121.723

† EVA FREUDOVÁ, born 14 January 1933;
deported 2 December 1941 and 4 October
1944.
D6 Small house in a wood
pastel on white paper: 16×26.5
Inscribed *Eva Freudová III.*
The house is decorated with heart-shaped
ornamentation and may be the 'gingerbread
cottage' of the Czech fairy-tale.
121.799

ANNA FLACHOVÁ, born 26 November 1931;
deported 2 December 1941.
D7 Tree in spring
watercolour on reverse of yellow paper:
25×13
Inscribed *28 B ANNA FLACH*.
121.822

† LENKA LINDTOVÁ, born 19 March 1930;
deported 15 February 1942 and 28 October
1944.
D8 Landscape with river and trees
collage of coloured paper: 14.5×19
Inscribed *Lenka Lindtheim 28 13 years*.
121.836

D9 Plants in a jam-jar
watercolour on reverse of yellow paper:
25×17.5
Inscribed *Lindt Lenka AU 429 L 410/28 14 years.*
121.840

† HELGA POLLAKOVÁ, born 11 December 1928;
deported 5 July 1943 and 19 October 1944.
D10 Landscape
watercolour on reverse of yellow paper:
25×34
Inscribed *H 18 Helga Pollak,* and on the verso
*Pure emotional drawing, the formal element totally
neglected.*
121.869

† ERIKA TAUSSIGOVÁ, born 28 October 1934;
deported 17 December 1941 and 16 October
1944.
D11 A vase of flowers and other sketches*
pencil and coloured crayons on reverse of
yellow paper: 24.5×17.5
Inscribed *Erika Taussig IV. b–24. V.1944.*
In the lower half is a yellow vase with three
flowers and a ladybird flying towards them,
and a blue dish containing eggs (?). Above is a
two-tiered Terezín bed with a child sleeping in
the upper bunk and another standing beside
the lower one. Above this is a rectangle with
various stains and the inscription *Sinai*.
121.976

† PETR WIEDMANN, born 1 September 1930;
deported 20 November 1942 and 4 October
1944.
D12 Landscape with three hills*
pencil and coloured crayons on yellow paper:
25×23
Inscribed *Wiedmann Petr 2.V.1944 13 1/4.*
Landscape showing three hills behind a cottage
with garden flanked by a row of trees. The
figures of a man and a child appear in the
foreground and the sun shines over a sailing
boat on the sea in the distance. On the reverse
is a drawing of a city square with skyscrapers
inscribed *CITY* with a box on the crossing
with a traffic policeman.
121.991

† EVA HESKÁ, born 29 May 1932;
deported 26 June 1942 and 18 May 1944.
D13 Tropical scene
pencil and crayon on reverse of yellow paper:
16.5×22.5
Inscribed *Eva Heská IV sk.*
In the middle stands a palm tree surrounded by
men in topee-like hats, with a camel with three
monkeys on its back, and exotic birds.
125.405

RAJA ENGLÄNDEROVÁ, born 25 August 1929;
deported 30 January 1942.
D14 Fear*
pencil on reverse of yellow paper: 22×28.5
Inscribed *Raja 25*.
Below a black gate, with a small round
window, perhaps symbolising imprisonment,
is the upper half of a figure in profile with
streaming hair and hands convulsively raised
towards its face with wide open eyes.
125.433

† KAREL SATTLER, born 16 November 1932;
deported 8 September 1942 and 4 October
1944.
D15 Burial scene*
pencil on yellow paper: 20.5×29
Inscribed *II.IV.4 Block 12 years Sattler.*
The house into which two men carry a coffin
is marked with a skull and crossbones and
inscribed *Burial*. To the right is the burial
procession of the family including a child
pushing a pram, the figures exclaiming *bé bé,* a

symbol of mourning. Above their heads is another skull and crossbones.
125.436.

† PAVEL SONNENSCHEIN, born 9 April 1931; deported 8 April 1942 and 23 October 1944.
D16 Terezín barracks*
watercolour on the reverse of technical drawing: 18.5×25.5
Inscribed *H II Sonnensch. 78.*
The drawing shows the empty courtyard of the Terezín barracks in which the deported were imprisoned.
125.515

† MARGARETA ZINNEROVÁ, born 9 August 1932; deported 18 February 1942 and 6 October 1944.
D17 Flowery meadow with butterfly
watercolour on yellow paper: 20.5×28.5
Inscribed on the verso *Zinner.*
125.517

† EVA KOHNOVÁ, born 20 April 1932; deported 5 July 1941 and 18 May 1944.
D18 Landscape
paper collage on yellow paper: 22.5×30.5
Inscribed *Eva Kohn 28.*
125.721

† JULIE OGULÁROVÁ, born 13 June 1933; deported 5 December 1942 and 6 October 1944.
D19 Winter scene
pencil and crayon on yellow paper: 20.5×29
Inscribed on the verso *Ogulár Julie 4 Block II.IV.*
Children are sledging down a hill towards a large snowman holding a broom; in the upper part of the drawing children are playing with a ball and pushing a pram. There are three houses with fenced gardens. On the verso is a large boat with a red triangular sail and a yellow-red flag on the stern. On the bow and stern stand three people.
125.732

† EVA BRUNNEROVÁ, born 27 August 1933; deported 19 March 1942 and 18 May 1944.
D20 Railway station
pencil and crayon on yellowish paper: 31×20
Inscribed *Eva Brunner 10 years.*
In the centre, a train is about to enter a tunnel. Below, a man selling sausages on the platform, a porter bringing luggage, a woman with luggage and two women in discussion. Above the track is a booking office, timetable, a man selling newspapers and two passengers. On the reverse is a pencil drawing of a similar scene with a greater number of passengers on the platform.
129.005

† MALVÍNA LÖWOVÁ, born 7 February 1932; deported 30 June 1942 and 19 October 1944.
D21 At home
crayon on reverse of yellow paper: 25.5×34.5
Inscribed *II. Löw Malvine.*
The interior of a room with two windows with curtains and flowers in pots; in the middle of the ceiling a lamp; on the right a bench with hats. Below to the left is a tiled stove. In the middle is a table with two chairs and two seated men with cups. To the right stand another three men and a woman.
129.093

† EDITA BIKKOVÁ, born 9 May 1933; deported 24 October 1942 and 23 October 1944.
D22 At home*
crayon on reverse of yellow paper: 25×35
Inscribed *Edita Bikkova H.13.*
In the centre of a room stands a woman at a table with a dish of dumplings and a vase of flowers, one boy in pyjamas standing to the left, another seated at the table, and a third writing sums on a board at the right. Behind are two windows with curtains and pots of flowers on the sills.
129.098

UNIDENTIFIED
D23 Terezín barracks and church tower at night*
watercolour on reverse of technical drawing: 21×29
Inscribed *Polach Dita.*
The drawing shows a characteristic view of the town which occurs more frequently in the work of the adult Terezín painters. The dark colours imaginatively suggest the forbidding atmosphere of the concentration camp.
129.214

† HANA KARPLUSOVÁ, born 4 January 1930; deported 4 April 1942 and 6 October 1944.
D24 The crossroads*
pencil and crayon on reverse of yellow paper: 23.5×24.5
Inscribed *Hana Karplus, II group.*
A lonely crossroads in a desolate landscape. A small fir plantation at the extreme left, and at the crossing a signpost inscribed *BRNO* pointing towards a small red house in the distance.
129.319

† EVA WOLLSTEINEROVÁ, born 24 January 1931; deported 8 April 1942 and 23 October 1944.
D25 Magdeburg barracks, Terezín*
pencil and crayon on yellowish paper: 20×30
Inscribed *IV. WOLLSTEINER EVA.*
The drawing shows the closed gate, barred lower windows, and part of the row of windows on the first floor of the Magdeburg barracks in Terezín, where the deported were held under arrest.
129.358

† RUTH HEINOVÁ, born 19 February 1934; deported 30 July 1942 and 23 October 1944.
D26 Village fair
crayon on yellowish paper: 16.5×20
Inscribed *Rut Hein*
In the centre is a merry-go-round, on the right an ice-cream stall. Around are swings and children. Upper left is a stall with the inscription *SWEETMEATS.*
129.364

† HANA NEUFELDOVÁ, born 1 March 1933; deported 22 February 1942 and 23 October 1944.

D27 Christmas at home
pencil and crayon on reverse of yellow paper: 32.5×23.5
Inscribed *Hana Neuteldová sk. V.30. dubna/April/1944.*
In the middle is a tall Christmas-tree with decorations and at the top a cross, flanked by a picture of flowers to the right, and a vase of flowers to the left. In front of the tree stands a child with presents addressed to: *Daddy, Mummy, Grandfather, Grandmother, Aunt, Eve, Lída, Many, Verka, Helena, Johnny and Soňa.*
129.365

† DORIS ZDEKAUEROVÁ, born 15 July 1932; deported 28 April 1942 and 16 October 1944.
D28 Princess and dragon*
pencil and crayon on yellowish paper: 19×31.5
Inscribed *Doris Zdekauerová, group III.*
A golden-haired princess is imprisoned in a cave by a winged dragon breathing fire. At the upper left is a figure with a pointed and tasselled cap.
129.371

† DORIT WEISEROVÁ, born 17 May 1932; deported 30 July 1944 and 4 October 1944.
D29 Butterfly in a meadow*
watercolour on yellowish paper: 16×21.5
Inscribed *Weiser Dorit 42*
The butterfly flies above a flowering meadow. This symbol of freedom occurs very frequently in the drawings of children from the Terezín concentration camp.
129.374

† JUDITA KLEINBERGEROVÁ, born 11 March 1933; deported 26 September 1942 and 6 October 1944.
D30 Three trees in a meadow
watercolour on reverse of yellow paper: 15×25
Inscribed *Judita Kleinbergerova I. group 27. June 6.*
129.399

HANA GRÜNFELDORÁ, born 20 May 1935; deported 14 February 1941.
D31 Interior at Terezín*
pencil and watercolour on yellow paper: 15×21
Inscribed *Hana Grünfeld VI. 1944 4 B.*
On the left is a three-tiered bunk, the beds marked *14, 15* and *16*. To the right of this is a table with two chairs and a jar of flowers.
129.406

ZUZANA ZEITSCHEKOVÁ, born 4 April 1932; deported 25 May 1942.
D32 Returning home
pencil and watercolour on the back of a geometrical drawing: 19.5×27
Inscribed *Zuzanne Zeitscheková.*
Six children walk along a road bordering a flowery meadow. The girl in front carries a red and white flag, inscribed *PRAGUE.*
129.683

† ILONA WEISSOVÁ, born 6 March 1932; deported 14 December 1941 and 15 May 1944.
D33 The land of plenty
pencil on yellow paper: 26.5×38
Inscribed *Ilona Weissová room 13.*
At the upper left is a banner inscribed *Entrance to the land of plenty – entrance fee 1 crown.* Below this, sitting on a bench, is a girl with a bird on a fork. To the right are lots of luxury foods, including bottles of punch and rum, a hedgehog with fruit stuck on to its spines and a fork in its rump, and a basket of eggs carried by a small winged figure.
129.706

† DORIS WEISSEROVÁ, born 17 May 1932; deported 30 June 1942 and 4 October 1944.
D34 Pot of flowers
embroidery on paper (printed form): 14.5×17.5
Inscribed *Doris Weisser.*
129.776

UNIDENTIFIED
D35 House and trees
collage of wood and fabric on paper (printed form): 17.5×14
129.786

† ROBERT BARDY, born 1 February 1932; deported 30 September 1942 and 6 October 1944.
D36 Landscape with two trees
watercolour on yellowish paper: 26×21.5
Inscribed *V. class Bardy.*
The two trees are sprouting new leaves.
130.778

†VERA LÖWYOVÁ, born 5 January 1931; deported 18 September 1942 and 19 October 1944.
D37 Cleaning*
pencil and crayon on grey paper: 22.5×31.5
Inscribed *13. IV. 44. V.Löwy 13 years V.*
The drawing shows the drying and beating of blankets, clothes and mattresses.
131.337

† HANA KALICHOVÁ, born 18 November 1931; deported 8 September 1942 and 15 May 1944.
D38 The supper of Seder
pencil and crayon on grey paper: 20×30.5
Inscribed *H. Kalich Anonym.*
Children and adults sit round a table with a white tablecloth. Around are the bunks of the concentration camp. On the reverse is a drawing of flowers in a vase.
133.042

Terezín painters

The collection of paintings from Terezín includes many works by adult artists, both amateur and professional. It is impossible to mention them all. Many portraits and minor drawings of Terezín interiors were made there with modest means and under improvised conditions. A frequent theme is the places of rest in the yards, where sparse vegetation and patches of blue sky provided the only contacts with nature in the camp. In this context, mention can be made of the watercolours by Ludwig Wodak, Moritz Nagel, and Leo Heilbron, drawings by Frantisek Zelenka, and also small pictures by a Dutchman, Jo Spier. Portraits were very popular. In the camp this was the only way to record the likeness of one's family. The artists of these portraits are for the most part unknown. The youngest, but artistically the most important mature painter in the camp, was Peter Klien, whose portraits of musicians are outstanding. In spite of constant insecurity and uncertainty, and the endless battle for existence, a certain intimate quality in his work indicates his attempts to make some sort of emotional response to the bleak world in which he found himself.

The core of the collection consists of pictures by several artists attempting to express their predicament through their art. Their work was based on critical observation of reality and of the events surrounding them. Their leading personality was Bedřich Fritta, a graphic artist and cartoonist from Prague. In the drawing office of a technical department at Terezín, he surrounded himself with artists such as Otto Ungar from Brno, Leo Haas from Opava, and Ferdinand Bloch, who lived in Prague before his deportation. Outside this group was a medical doctor, Karel Fleischmann from Ceské Budejovice, who worked in a Terezín medical care centre. These artists were courageous not only creatively but also personally, for they had to keep their activity secret and few fellow-prisoners knew about it. After an unsuccessful attempt to smuggle out of the camp a collection of drawings depicting the reality of conditions there, four draughtsmen from the technical department were accused of spreading 'horror propaganda' and were deported along with their families on 17 July 1944. Karel Fleischmann was also deported shortly after these four. Bloch died in the Small Fort at Terezín; Fritta died in Auschwitz in August, and Fleischmann, also in Auschwitz, in October. Ungar was crippled, and died in 1945, shortly after the liberation of Buchenwald.

More than 600 drawings by Karel Fleischmann, now in the Museum's collection, provide a sequence of vividly graphic 'snapshots' portraying daily life at Terezín. The arrivals and departures of the transports, which set the rhythm of life in the camp and affected every individual, are his main themes. We see crowds of tired, stooping prisoners, carrying heavy baggage into the night, dragging their possessions along with enormous effort, and finally waiting in dark cellars for their next journey. Fleischmann does not depict individuals but crowds – masses controlled by some inner hectic movement. Life in the camp is given an impersonal character which documents the degradation of the prisoners and their subordination to strange, inhuman forces.

Bedřich Fritta represents a different type of artist – one with a strong intellect and a powerful imagination. By starting with a number of small sketches of his subject, he could create a larger drawing with absolute certainty. He selected only certain elements from reality. These he then distorted in order to express their full meaning. In his interpretation, a new depth and symbolism emerged from quite ordinary themes. Again and again, he repeated the motifs of a leafless tree, of the bastions of the Terezín fortifications, of abandoned baggage, of the figure of a blind man, of a hearse used for transporting old and sick prisoners, of endless transports extending to a horizon of waste-land. These works of art derived from his experience of the absurdity and unreality of life – a world devoid of meaning and therefore of hope. His was a fantastic metaphor for a world being destroyed by the horrors of war.

The art of Otto Ungar differed from that of Fleischmann and Fritta. He was, above all, a painter. He used tempera, watercolour, or gouache in a spirited way, and his compositions followed traditional lines. His paintings are unusually monumental and dramatic and are executed in harmonious dark colours.

Most of the drawings by Leo Haas are now in the Terezín Memorial Collection. Like Fritta, he depicts with uncompromising criticism hospitals, cripples, crowded barracks, and blind prisoners.

Only a few drawings by Ferdinand Bloch have been preserved. Like the others mentioned, he portrays silent crowds awaiting transportation, and the events of the barracks – peeling potatoes in the yards, the last farewell to the dead, the improvisation of religious services in attics. These scenes are presented without pathos. They testify to the artist's deep understanding of the human suffering in the camp.

These five artists from Bohemia, Moravia, and Silesia, who met at Terezín in 1942, had different backgrounds and developed differently as artists. Nevertheless, we find in their works a similar interest in the same themes and a certain resemblance in artistic expression – sharp contrasts of light, for example, dark tones and an inner dramatic tension of line. These characteristics of the Terezín paintings relate them to works created in Brno and Prague at the time of the Protectorate. They are particularly close to the work of a group of artists calling themselves 'Seven in October' which originated in Prague in 1939.

Karel Fleischmann: The first night's sleep

D48 Bedřich Fritta: View looking towards the
Terezín ghetto

D50 Bedřich Fritta: A transportation leaving
the ghetto for the railway station in
Buhušovice

D56 Leo Haas: Interior view of women's accommodation

D57 Leo Haas: Prisoners walking in a park

† KAREL FLEISCHMANN, born in Klatovy 1897; deported April 1942 and October 1944; died in Osvětim.

† BEDŘICH FRITTA, born 1909; deported December 1941 and July 1944; died in Osvětim.

D39 Prisoners awaiting deportation*
(front cover)
pen, brush and Indian ink: 35×45.3
Signed, dated and inscribed *Terezín KF 43*.
In the cellars of the Terezín barracks, the lying and standing prisoners await deportation to the Polish extermination camps.
175.161

D40 Prisoners carrying children and luggage
brush and Indian ink: 29×41
Signed, dated and inscribed *Terezín KF 43*.
175.358

D41 The first night's sleep*
black crayon: 30×44
Signed and dated *KF 42*.
After arrival at Terezín, prisoners are sleeping on the ground before being allocated their huts. They are crammed beside each other with their luggage and are wrapped in their coats with their hats or caps on their heads.
175.369

D42 Prisoners leaving and arriving at Terezín*
black crayon: 30.3×43.8
Signed and dated *KF 42*.
On the Terezín road a row of bent figures with bags on their backs walking into the night, beyond them a group of people pulling a cart laden with luggage and old prisoners on their way to Terezín.
175.371

D43 Queuing for a meal
Indian ink: 29×28.8
Signed, dated and inscribed *Terezín KF 43*.
Five lean figures, marked with the six-pointed Star of David on the left side of their chests, are standing in line with vessels in their hands. This is a characteristic picture of life in the Terezín camp.
175.374

D44 Infirm and dead prisoners
Indian ink: 22.5×32
Inscribed and dated *Terezín 43* and signed and dated *KF 43*.
A cart, pulled by a man at night, brings in aged prisoners from Germany, some of whom are ill or already dead.
175.397

D45 Children going for a walk
Indian ink on note-book paper: 15×20.7
Signed and dated *KF 42*.
Children were only allowed to go out for a walk for a short while. A group of them in coats and caps, holding hands, are here looking helplessly around on the deserted Terezín road in Autumn.
175.402

D46 Three men awaiting transportation*
Indian ink: 20.4×27
In the foreground lies a sick man wrapped in a blanket; behind him are two men, one seated, the other (who is blind) standing and groping with his stick. A knapsack and two suitcases are marked with the numbers of the transportation.
174.045

D47 Male workers' barracks
Indian ink: 38×28.5
Signed *Fritta*.
An interior view of the Terezín barracks peopled with the inmates, many of whom are lying or seated on three-tier bunks which recede in steep perspective towards the trellised window at the opposite end of the room. The foreground is dominated by the resigned figure of a half-naked man seated on a stool.
174.087

D48 View looking towards the Terezín ghetto*
Indian ink: 40×58
174.133

D49 An old Jewish burial carriage transporting old and sick prisoners
Indian ink: 40×58
174.139

D50 A transportation leaving the ghetto for the railway station in Buhusovice*
Indian ink: 48×72
174.146

D51 Emergency accommodation for the old in the prisons of Terezín
Indian ink: 27.5×38
Signed *Fritta*.
These buildings were used whenever the camp became overcrowded.
174.171

† FERDINAND BLOCH, born 15 August 1898; deported 30 July 1942; died in the Small Stronghold of Terezín.

LEO HAAS, born 1901; deported 30 September 1942 and 1944 to Osvětim.

OTTO UNGAR, born 27 November 1901; deported 1942 and 1944 to Osvětim; died 25 July 1945.

D52 A crowd of the deported awaiting transportation on the Terezín road
pencil and watercolour: 33.5×41
Inscribed *feb 1942*.
173.811

D53 A Jewish burial ceremony at Terezín
black crayon: 30.5×38.5
Inscribed *feb Theresienstadt 1943*.
Mourners and elders deliver their farewell orations to the coffins of the dead, piled in the corridor of a cellar at Terezín.
173.813

D54 A group of elderly seated women scraping potatoes in the barracks yard at Terezín
charcoal: 40×32
Inscribed *Terezín 1942* and *feb*.
Potatoes were the main source of food in Terezín.
174.244

D55 Interior view of women's accommodation at Terezín
Indian ink: 27×34
Inscribed *feb TEREZÍN 1943*.
174.776

D56 Interior view of women's accommodation*
Indian ink: 60×44.5
Signed and inscribed *28.VIII.43 Leo Haas*.
173.557

D57 Prisoners walking in a park*
Indian ink: 38×50
Inscribed *4.VIII.43*.
The drawing depicts a group of prisoners who are temporarily allowed to enter a former park for exercise.
173.558

D58 Sick people in a prison hospital
Indian ink: 38.5×50
Inscribed *4.VIII.1943*.
173.559

D59 Two elderly men standing together
gouache: 60×44.5
The mens' jackets bear yellow Stars of David; the building, in front of which they are standing, is numbered *Q307*.
173.562

D60 Women queuing for food
gouache: 42×58
The women wear the Star of David on the left side of their coats.
173.566

D61 Interior view of lodging 'AA 32'
gouache: 50.5×70
On the reverse of this drawing is an imaginary night scene depicting three old women and a pile of coffins.
175.776

The Museum's collection of textiles is unique both for its size (there are about 10,000 items) and quality. Sets of woven and embroidered textiles of extraordinary value provide a chronological sequence from the end of the Renaissance to the beginning of the twentieth century.

The term 'synagogue textiles' comprises the Torah curtains (singular, *parochet*), Torah pelmets (singular, *kapporet*), and Torah mantles (singular, *me'il*), used in synagogues. Their main function is to protect and to decorate the parchment scrolls of the Torah (the Pentateuch or Five Books of Moses) which are usually covered with a mantle and kept in a sanctuary (the *Aron ha-kodesh* or Ark of the Law). A curtain and a pelmet are hung over the sanctuary both to decorate and to protect it.

The design of synagogue textiles is dictated by religious tradition. In the course of history, it became normal for it to approximate to the architecture of the sanctuary itself. A rectangular centre-piece, usually of a costly woven or embroidered cloth, was inserted between two columns decorated with vine tendrils. The upper part of the textile bears a Hebrew dedication giving the name of the donor; sometimes the names of his wife or other members of the family were also added. The inscription might also be enriched with short quotations from traditional literature, and with information concerning the occasion for which the textile was made and the year in which it was given to the synagogue. The textiles were decorated with various traditional symbols (seven-branched candlesticks, the Tables of the Law, Levite jugs, the table with bread, the blessing hands of the priests, Cohenin) or other motifs such as lions bearing crowns. In some cases these symbols decorate only the pelmet hanging over the curtain. Such an example is a pelmet from Brno, dated 1740 (cat. T1).

A study of the Museum's textile collection shows that during the late sixteenth and the seventeenth centuries expensive and rich materials were used. In view of the fact that in many instances the material is over a hundred years older than the curtains themselves, we can conclude that the antiquity of the material is considerable. The situation changed somewhat around 1700 when inventories of synagogues show that practically contemporary fabrics were appearing besides older ones. The reason for this was not so much a change in synagogue traditions as a change in textile production and in the trade as a whole. The rapid development in the technology of the time enabled new designs to be produced more easily. This production of new designs led to the popularity of new fashions. Garments more than one year old lost a third of their original price and the nobility discarded them. The trade in second-hand garments explains why synagogue textiles are often stitched together from uneven pieces. Sometimes it is even possible to trace the cut of the original garment.

In any reference to the textile trade, it is worth remarking that in Bohemia the import of textiles had been in the hands of Jewish merchants from the seventeenth century, and was controlled by them during the whole of the eighteenth century. It is not surprising, therefore, that synagogues were provided with the best materials available at the time.

The ritual objects of synagogues also included velvets and brocades in a variety of designs, which reflected the development of European textile patterns. Fabrics of French origin are more frequent than Spanish or Italian ones.

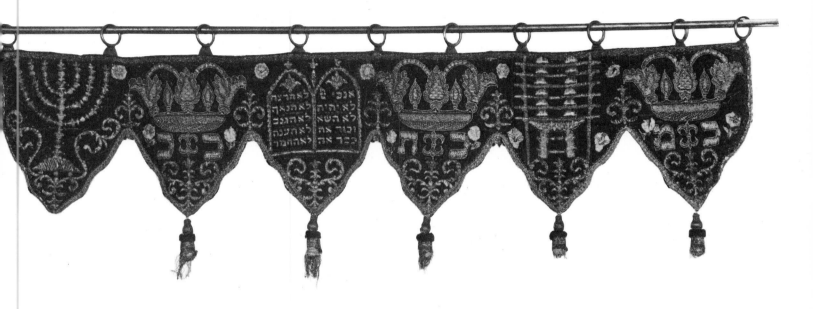

T1 Pelmet, Moravia: Brno, 1740

T2 Pelmet, Moravia: Brno, 1762

The collection contains several attractive brocades with the so-called 'lace pattern', made in France between 1690 and 1730. Lace silk was used for a mantle from Nový Bydzov, exhibited here and dated 1750 (cat. T23). A French fabric with a design combining a 'bizarre' pattern and naturalistic floral ornament was popular in the 1720s. This kind of silk was used on a mantle from Turnov, dated 1735 (cat. T20). Another example of a French silk is seen on a mantle from the Pinkas Synagogue in Prague with an inscription dated 1671 (cat. T18). This silk fabric with a pattern imitating a fur boa was made in the period of Queen Maria Lesczinska in the mid-eighteenth century. The mantle itself, which is from the end of the seventeenth century, was obviously later mended with new silk. We can therefore conclude that the year inscribed on a synagogue textile does not necessarily determine how old the textile is. As we have seen, sometimes the material used is substantially older than this. Sometimes damaged textiles were later repaired with new fabrics.

The Baroque era began in Bohemia in the late seventeenth century and Baroque silver-gilt thread embroidery was used on a large scale on velvet, as well as rich brocades in a variety of designs. Several of these embroidered textiles, made between 1697 and 1740, are exhibited (cat. T8, T9, T10, T21). The compositions, in embroidered high relief, display Baroque feeling, and new Baroque elements – twisted columns and acanthus leaves – are used in the decoration. However, the restraint of the whole design means that the optical and dynamic tendencies of the Baroque style are not fully displayed. It is clear from all this that the assessment of textiles in terms of their historic and artistic qualities requires a different approach to that used for other art objects in the collection.

On the whole, the textiles of the synagogue remained immune from the pressures of fashion. They were, above all, religious objects. Their decoration was subordinated to tradition. The artistic quality of the work, its splendour and its costliness, reflected the donor's devotion to God, his status in the religious community, as well as his own standards of taste. However, if we are to judge these textiles by their artistic character, their quality of workmanship, and the material used, we can divide them into three groups.

First are pieces obviously worked by those with skilled hands, a knowledge of complicated techniques and access to expensive materials which were usually presented by prominent members of the Jewish community. They often served as models and sources of inspiration for later works. An example of this from the collection is a Renaissance curtain for the Ark which was decorated in appliqué. This use of appliqué in curtains was probably first adopted by the Perlstiker family in Prague. It was also favoured by Mordecai Maisel, Mayor of the Prague Jewish Town in the late sixteenth century, who had ordered a similar curtain to be made, which he later gave to the synagogue that he had founded. These curtains were so influential that appliqué curtains were very popular in the Prague Jewish community during the whole of the seventeenth century. Their influence can even be seen on an Ark curtain from the end of the seventeenth century (cat. T6) which is dated 1687 and was given to the Alt-Neu

---

13 Pelmet, Bohemia: Březnice, 1812

15 Pelmet, Bohemia: Prague (The Jewish
Council of Elders), 1867

Synagogue in Prague by Wolf Anshil to replace an older curtain given by a relative. The way in which earlier schemes of decoration influenced later ones can also be seen in two mantles from Nový Bydzov (cat. T22 and T24). The first was made in 1743. The second was given to the synagogue in 1765 by the then Mayor of the Jewish community at Nový Bydzov. Both are almost identically framed with a Hebrew inscription, and obviously the decoration of the first inspired that of the second. From about 1740, mantles contain beautiful pieces of French Rococo brocade.

The second group of textiles shows the influence of folk art. They were usually made at home by the donors themselves. They reflect the feeling of country people for decoration and the poetic organisation of ornament. Produced away from the main stream of culture, they bring in a new decorative style. The materials used were linen, felt, pieces of silk from Sunday-best clothes, or small fragments of expensive fabrics. These were embellished with home-made decorations – bobbin lace, buttons, souvenirs such as cockades and the badges of army uniforms, and various forms of trimming. Traditional Biblical symbols were still used and the decorative style tended to be traditional, but folk-art elements were used more freely. These included floral motifs and hearts and pigeons, as used in the decoration of domestic textiles and folk costumes.

A modest example on exhibition is a mantle from Horovice dated 1843 (cat. T25). It is made of white linen and embroidered in red and white yarn in plain stitch with buttonhole ('Richelieu') embroidery. This technique was very popular in the Bohemian countryside. Another example of the folk-art approach to decoration is a curtain dated 1832 (cat. T14). It is made of silk satin, decorated with silver thread, and with additions most probably taken from some older curtain. It represents an increase in the influence of rustic themes upon traditional textile decoration.

The last group comprises textiles made in the nineteenth and twentieth centuries. Their main characteristic is that they were mass-produced and were decorated by means of stencils. The perfection of their manufacture is surprising, but the only rôle of the donors was to choose the material and the pattern from a pattern book.

Textiles for synagogues at the beginning of the twentieth century were made of contemporary modern fabrics (mantles, cat. T28 and T29) or from household materials like table-cloths and carpets. They were decorated in a simple way with a limited number of traditional symbols.

T12 Curtain, Moravia: Brno, 1st half of 19th century

115 Curtain, Bohemia: Kolín, 1832

נ״ז
הקצין כ״ה יורה יחי׳
ואשתו מרת חנה קויפריד תפ׳
ש׳ ת״ר״י״ג לפ״ק

116 Curtain, Bohemia: Jindřichův Hradec, 1853

117 Mantle, Bohemia: Prague (Maisel
Synagogue), 1658

120 Mantle, Bohemia: Turnov, 1735

T21 Mantle, Provenance unknown, 1740

127 Mantle, Bohemia: Prague (Jerusalem Synagogue), 1862

קֹדֶשׁ לַיָי

כֹּל הָאִשָּׁה הַחֲשׁוּבָה מ׳ סעדל
אלמנת מו״ה וואלף באשעלעס ול
לזכרון נשמה בעלה המנוח
ביום חתונת בתה
הבתולה מ׳ בונא
עם הבח׳ כה׳ יעקב
יפן המנוח כה׳ בצלאל סגל ז״ל
ביום ב׳ מרחשון
שנת תרכ״ג
לפ״ק

T29 Mantle, Bohemia: Volyně, c.1900

T37 Wrapper, Moravia: Loětice, 1750

T40 Wrapper, Bohemia: Domažlice, 1815

T41 Wrapper, Bohemia: Přeštice, 1856

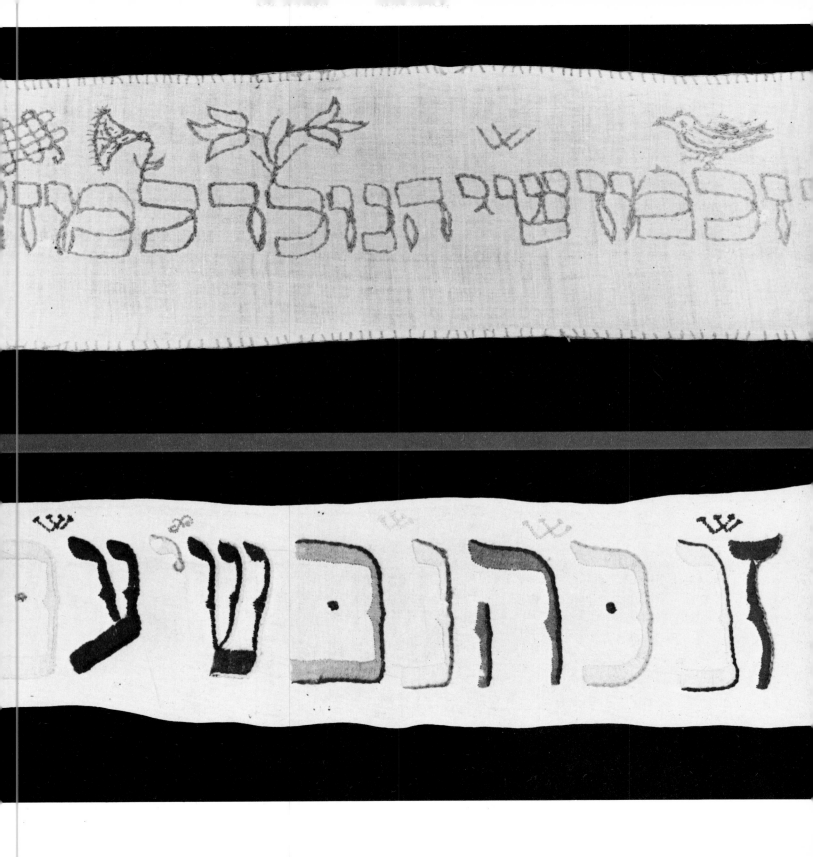

PELMETS (singular, KAPPORET)

T1 Pelmet *
Moravia: Brno, 1740
Velvet, trimmed with braid, with Vandyke
lower edge, each indentation ending in a tassel;
relief embroidery in silver thread. Each
partition carries a symbolic motif, left to right:
candlestick, crown, the Tables of The Law,
crown, shew bread, crown, with leaf and
tendril ornament.
30×136
5.169b

T2 Pelmet*
Moravia: Brno, 1762
Red velvet, with Vandyke lower edge,
trimmed all round with braid, and relief
embroidery in gold thread. Each indentation
supports a leaf, palmette and flower spray on
corded stems, enclosed in a border of
alternating scrolls and acanthus leaves.
49×154
5.166

T3 Pelmet*
Bohemia: Březnice, 1812
Green and brown velvet with appliqué,
fastened with couching, and relief embroidery
in metal thread. Two large and two pendant
small scallops at the lower edge, fringed. Top
centre, an applied band with a three-line
Hebrew inscription, giving the donor's name,
embroidered in metal thread.
44×126
59.890

T4 Pelmet
Moravia, 1st half of 19th century
Blue velvet with a pattern of brocaded gold
acanthus leaves and printed leaf tendrils,
trimmed with braid, with deep, fringed
scallops at the lower edge. A band of dark
brown velvet applied across the centre has a
one-line Hebrew inscription in gold braid,
giving the donor's name.
35×144
12.027

T5 Pelmet*
Bohemia: Prague (The Jewish Council of
Elders), 1867
White silk with woven checks of red, blue,
green and brown. The pelmet is curved at the
top, scalloped at the lower edge and trimmed
all round with a silk fringe. A central panel of
applied red velvet, edged with gold braid, has a
Hebrew inscription, embroidered in gold
thread: *Holy Unto The Lord*
50×104
46.253

ARK CURTAINS (singular, PAROCHET)

T6 Curtain colour plate I
Bohemia: Prague (Alt-Neu Synagogue), 1687
Green velvet with relief embroidery in silver
thread, cords and sequins. Top centre, a
crown, floral ornament and a five-line Hebrew
inscription, giving the names of the donors,
Mr and Mrs ?Mieroles, from Vienna, and
recording the renewal of the curtain by their
grandchildren. The inscription is flanked by
vertical leaf ornament, in the form of columns,
surmounted by crowns. Lower borders have
rows of detached stylised flower sprays.
Centre panel of black silk, edged with braid,
with an embroidered repeat pattern of curving
stems and small flowers, heavily encrusted
with sequins.
220×160
27.360

T7 Curtain colour plate II
Bohemia: Prague (Pinkas Synagogue), 1689
Dark red velvet, trimmed with braid, with
relief embroidery in silver and gold thread. At
the top, a four-line Hebrew inscription, giving
the donor's name, flanked by a coat-of-arms
above a stylised urn with flowers standing on a
winged plinth. Centre panel, edged with braid
and, on three sides, with floral silk, is of red
satin embroidered with all-over repeat pattern
of pairs of curved, serrated leaves supporting
ears of corn.
220×159
12.681

T8 Curtain
Bohemia, 1689 and 1696
Red velvet, trimmed with fringed braid, with
relief embroidery in silver and gold thread.
Top, a four-line Hebrew inscription, giving
the donor's name, flanked by 'columns' in the
form of vertically repeated palmettes, foliage
and tendrils; coronet capitals are surmounted
by urns with flowers and foliage. Lower
border has the same ornament as the
'columns'. Centre panel of red satin, edged
with braid, has an all-over floral and ribbon
repeat pattern worked in silver passementerie.
230×158
27.398

T9 Curtain
Bohemia: Prague (Pinkas Synagogue), 1697
Dark red velvet with relief embroidery in
silver and gold thread. Top, centre, a four-line
Hebrew inscription, giving the donor's name,
flanked by twisted columns, wreathed with
vine stems and grapes, with elongated capitals
of acanthus, crowns and urns holding flower
sprays. Between the column bases a panel of
scrolling acanthus leaves springing from a
central palmette. Centre panel, edged with
braid, embroidery of a slightly later date with
an all-over scrolling repeat.
231×163
12.684

T10 Curtain colour plate III
Bohemia: Mladá Boleslav, 1702
Red velvet with relief embroidery in silver and
gold thread. Top, centre, a four-line Hebrew
inscription, giving the donor's name, flanked
by twisted columns, wreathed with vine stems
and grapes, with foliated capitals surmounted
by urns holding flower sprays. Column bases
and lower border have scrolling stem and
flower patterns. Centre panel, edged with
braid, is embroidered with an all-over repeat
of scrolling stems and leaves bearing
palmettes, with coronets at the intersections.
230×150
2.240

T11 Curtain
Bohemia: Prague (Alt-Neu Synagogue), 1716
Brown velvet with relief embroidery in metal
thread. Top, a three-line Hebrew memorial
inscription. Centre panel of rose-pink floral
silk, edged with lace.
217×147
27.380

T12 Curtain*
Moravia: Brno, 1st half of 19th century
Beige silk with appliqué of urns and plant
ornament.
127×127
3.251

T13 Curtain
Moravia: Boskovice, 1814
Green and blue silk with woven repeat of
small, conventionalised flower sprays in gold.
Lower frill of gathered plain silk, ending in a
tasselled fringe. Centre panel of light blue silk,
with a woven half-drop floral repeat pattern in
pink, blue and green, is ornamented at the top
with insignia from an officer's uniform of the
reign of Emperor Francis I; below, a three-line
Hebrew inscription, giving the donor's name
and the date, and the Star of David.
126×86
2.900

T14 Curtain
Moravia: Boskovice, 1832
Blue satin with appliqué of dark brown velvet
and embroidery in silver thread. Centre panel,
flanked by wreathed columns and arcades has,
top, a crown beneath draperies, below, two
addorsed lions flanking a small crown and a
seven-line Hebrew inscription, giving the
donor's name, and below: *Renew Our Days As
Of Old*. At the lower edge, three eight-lobed
rosettes and a linear pattern in passementerie.
178×114
2.896a

T15 Curtain*
Bohemia: Kolín, 1832
Rose silk floral damask, edged with fringed
braid, embroidered in gold thread. Top, a
six-line Hebrew inscription, giving the
donor's name, flanked by urns bearing the Star

of David and holding flower sprays. Centre
panel of yellow brocaded damask with a small
half-drop repeat of stylised flower sprays,
edged with patterned braid.
186×126
52.616

T16 Curtain*
Bohemia: Jindřichův Hradec, 1853
White silk, trimmed with ruched braid, with
embroidery in coloured silks and gold thread.
Centre, enclosed in a cartouche of twisted
cord, a four-line Hebrew inscription, giving
the donor's name and the date. A coloured
floral spray in each corner.
148×97
40.434

TORAH MANTLES (singular, ME'IL)

T17 Mantle*
Bohemia: Prague (Maisel Synagogue), 1658
Upper part of light brown velvet, fringed,
with relief embroidery in metal thread, has a
three-line Hebrew inscription, giving the
donor's name and the date. Lower part of
purple satin, French, mid-18th century,
brocaded with a vertical repeat of columns,
scrolls and delicate plant ornament in yellow,
blue and green. Tassel fringe at the two side
edges.
93×52
31.874

T18 Mantle colour plate IV, a
Bohemia: Prague (Pinkas Synagogue), 1671
The upper part, earliest in date, of dark red
velvet, divided into three bands by fringes,
with relief embroidery in silver thread, has a
three-line Hebrew inscription, giving the
donor's name and the date. Side and lower
borders of green figured velvet. Centre panel
of French mid-18th century ribbed silk
brocade with voided velvet pile, with 'fur boa'
and flower repeat.
89×48
52.527

T19 Mantle
Bohemia: Kolín, 1690
Red silk damask with an all-over repeat of urns
and stylised floral ornament, banded with
braid and embroidered in ochre silk. Top, a
four-line Hebrew inscription, giving the
donor's name. The lower panels have
embroidered single bell-shaped flowers and
fruit in the upper corners and eight-pointed
star-flowers in the outer lower corners.
45×92
61.506

T20 Mantle*
Bohemia: Turnov, 1735
Light brown velvet, edged with fringed braid,
relief embroidery in silver and gold thread.
Top, a three-line Hebrew inscription:
*Righteous women of the Congregation of
Turnov/The Law of the Lord is Perfect* and the
date. Centre panel, edged with ruched metal
braid, of silk brocade with a 'bizarre' design,
French, 1720s.
88×50
57.270

T21 Mantle*
Provenance unknown, 1740
Red velvet, edged with fringed braid, with
relief embroidery in silver and gold thread.
Narrow outer leaf border encloses at the top a
three-line Hebrew inscription giving the
donor's name and the date. Centre panel, also
embroidered, has a symmetrical design of
strapwork, floral and foliage ornament.
90×50
101.890

T22 Mantle colour plate V
Bohemia: Bydžov, 1743
Green velvet, edged with fringed braid, with
relief embroidery in gold thread. Top, a leafy
wreath encloses a crown and a Hebrew
inscription: *The Crown Of The Torah/Holy
Unto The Lord*. Below, embroidered twisted
columns, wreathed in leaves, with bulbous
capitals, and a lower border of leaves springing
from a pomegranate. Centre panel, edged with
braid, of light brown silk, French, mid-18th
century, brocaded in gold with a delicate floral
repeat.
92×49
65.927

T23 Mantle
Bohemia: Nový Bydžov, 1750
Upper part of brown velvet edged with braid, with embroidery in metal thread, has a three-line inscription giving the donor's name. Lower part of red velvet of later date, edged with braid, and centre panel of French silk brocade, mid-18th century, with an all-over floral repeat in yellow, pink and gold.
90×50
65.916

T24 Mantle colour plate IV, b
Bohemia: Nový Bydžov, 1765
Dark red velvet edged with gold braid, and relief embroidery in gold and silver thread. Top, enclosed in a leafy wreath, a four-line Hebrew inscription, naming the donor's wife. Centre panel, edged with braid, of French silk brocade with a floral repeat.
88×52
65.917

T25 Mantle
Bohemia: Hořovice, 1843
Undyed linen, embroidered. Border of eight-lobed rosettes in cutwork ('Richelieu' work), in self-coloured linen thread. Lower border of hand-made netted fringe. Top, centre, embroidered in red, a crown and looped cords above the Star of David, which encloses a four-line Hebrew inscription giving the name of the donor.
95×50
5.699

T26 Mantle
Bohemia: Vodňany, 1855
Mantle of the Sephardi type, of dark red velvet, edges and seams outlined with gold braid, fringed at the lower edge. Embroidery in silver thread. Centre, a crown with above, in outline, a crown flanked by a pair of confronted lions, and one-line Hebrew inscription: *Crown of The Torah*. Below, a six-line Hebrew inscription, giving the name of the donors, the Kafka family, flanked by two classical urns.
66; oval top 30×22
49.454

T27 Mantle*
Bohemia: Prague (Jerusalem Synagogue), 1862
Black velvet, edged with floral braid, with 'needle-painting' embroidery in coloured silks. Top, a crown surmounted by a one-line Hebrew inscription: *Holy Unto The Lord*. Below, centre, a ten-line dedicatory Hebrew inscription by the donor in memory of her husband, on the occasion of her daughter's marriage. In each corner, sprays of roses, pinks and other flowers.
90×52
31.801

T28 Mantle
Bohemia: Kolín, c.1880
Green wool with woven chequered stripes of red, blue and white, self-fringed. Centre panel, outlined by applied braid, has an embroidered Star of David, from which is suspended a crown and a Hebrew inscription: *Holy Unto The Lord*. Ribbon bows at the side edges.
63×47
71.211

T29 Mantle*
Bohemia: Volyně, c.1900
Blue silk with woven black and white stripes, edges and central design of light brown lace, applied. Centre, the Star of David. Trimming of ribbon bows.
85×49
23.314b

COVERS

T30 Cover
Bohemia: Sealčany, 1824
Undyed linen with embroidery in coloured thread. Border and centre have Hebrew inscriptions with the names of the donors.
86×72
5.229f

T31 Cover for Sabbath Bread
Provenance unknown, 2nd half of 19th century
Undyed linen of oval shape, with embroidery in coloured thread. Outer border in cutwork embroidery in the form of periwinkle flowers.

In the centre the Sabbath Bread, enclosed by a Hebrew inscription: *Blessing Of The Bread*.
Diameter: 44
8175

T32 Cover* (back cover)
Bohemia: Prague (Synagogue in Karlín), 2nd half of 19th century
Dark yellow silk with corded edges and printed design. In the centre, the Star of David is enclosed in a Hebrew inscription: *Let him kiss me with the kisses of his mouth: for thy love is better than wine*. (The Song of Solomon I. v.2) Surrounding this, and linked to it by cords, 12 medallions with the names of the Tribes of Israel and their symbols:

Reuben	*Simeon*	*Levi*	*Judah*
Benjamin			*Zebulun*
Joseph			*Issachar*
Naftali	*Asher*	*Gad*	*Dan*

Outer border has Hebrew inscription: top and bottom: *And Israel shall keep The Sabbath;* left side: *Come my beloved to Greet the Bride;* right side: *To Welcome in the Sabbath tide.*
51×50
65.689

T33 Matzot cover
Bohemia: Prague (Treuhandstelle), end of 19th century
Undyed linen of rectangular shape, with scalloped buttonhole edging, embroidered in coloured thread. The cover is divided into four rectangular panels, each with a different scene: 1). The one who does not know how to ask. The simple one. 2). The wicked one. The wise one. 3). The wine cup and dish of bitter herbs, enclosed in an Aramaic inscription: *This is the Bread of Poverty which our Fathers ate in the Land of Egypt*. 4). The Star of David and Hebrew inscription: *of the Passover*.
37×127
52.142

T34 Cover for Sabbath Bread*
Moravia: Mikulov, end of 19th century
Undyed linen with embroidery in undyed and
coloured thread. Outer edge of maple leaves in
cutwork, inner border of maple leaves and
flowers, embroidered with coloured threads in
line stitches. Centre, a three-line Hebrew
inscription for the Blessing of the Bread.
58×70
4.872

T35 Cover (not in exhibition)
Provenance unknown, c.1900
Undyed linen with warp-fringes, and
embroidery in coloured thread. Upper and
lower borders have one-line Hebrew
inscriptions: upper, *The Passover of Unleavened
Bread and Bitter Herbs;* lower, *Next Year In
Jerusalem.*
Centre medallion in the form of a Hebrew
inscription, giving the Blessing on eating the
unleavened bread at Passover.
137×52
82.060a

T36 Cover for Sabbath Bread
Moravia (Museum of Moravia), c.1900
Undyed linen with a red floral border. Over
the entire field a printed Hebrew text, the
Kiddush, benediction over wine for the Sabbath
and festivals.
90.5×83
4.873

TORAH WRAPPERS (MAPPOT)

T37 Wrapper*
Moravia: Loětice, 1750
Undyed linen with 'needle-painting'
embroidery in coloured threads. Outer
borders of flowers and scrolling acanthus
leaves enclose part of a Hebrew inscription: *the
good and modest woman . . .*
16×301.7
10.130

T38 Wrapper
Provenance unknown
Undyed linen with edges buttonhole-stitched
and embroidery in coloured threads. The
wrapper has been made from a baby's
swaddling cloth and the one-line Hebrew
inscription expresses congratulations on the
baby's birth, with rustic floral ornament.
11.5×320
10.164

T39 Wrapper
Bohemia: Domažlice, c.1st half of 19th century
Undyed linen with edges buttonhole-stitched
and embroidery in red and blue cotton. Made
from a baby's swaddling cloth, with a Hebrew
inscription giving the baby's name,
embellished with plant ornament.
15×273
28.249/2

T40 Wrapper*
Bohemia: Domažlice, 1815
Undyed linen with edges buttonhole-stitched
and embroidery in red and blue cotton. Made
from a baby's swaddling cloth, with a
fragmentary Hebrew inscription, giving the
baby's name, embellished with plant
ornament, birds and fish.
15.5×289
28.249/1

T41 Wrapper*
Bohemia: Přeštice, 1856
Undyed linen with embroidery in coloured
threads. Made from a baby's swaddling cloth,
with a fragmentary Hebrew inscription giving
the baby's name.
11×262
52.881

Objects in precious and other metals

After the textiles, the second largest collection in the State Jewish Museum is that of metalwork. It numbers almost 8,000 items, and, though diverse, it has its own historic, cultural, and artistic quality that makes it in many ways unique.

Most of the objects are of silver, but tin, brass, copper, German silver and common metals are also used. A few pieces are of gold. Most objects were made for use in the synagogue or for religious celebrations at home, but there are some for personal use. The objects from synagogues are principally represented by Torah breastplates, finials, crowns, pointers, Levite sets, and different kinds of lamps. The characteristic items for home celebrations are Sabbath spice boxes, Sabbath lamps, cups used for various occasions (circumcision, Passover feast, etc), Passover plates, *etrog* boxes, silver cases for the scrolls of the Book of Esther, circumcision sets, *mezuzot,* amulets and so on. The collection also includes silver combs, toilet articles, alms boxes, and collection plates, originally belonging to the Burial Brotherhood (*Ḥevra Kadisha*), and also a small collection of jewellery, mainly rings.

These objects reflect developments in the workshops that crafted gold, silver and pewter, from the seventeenth to the beginning of the twentieth centuries. There are also silver and pewter products from Vienna, Nuremberg, Augsburg and Galicia. About two-thirds of the items – mostly those used for ritual purposes – have dedicatory inscriptions in Hebrew. These inscriptions, together with makers' marks, help to date the objects.

From the beginning of the seventeenth century there is an increasing use of decorative motifs on silver objects in synagogues. This, together with the adoption of figures in ornamentation, is similar to the trend in the decoration of Torah curtains and mantles. It is most clearly illustrated in the Torah breastplates in the collection and these particularly excel in quality of design and technique. It is interesting to observe the reaction of their makers to the Rococo style, which is indifferent to ornamental symmetry and prefers the playful and the curvacious. In their turn, both Baroque and Rococo breastplates later give way to Classicism and the two twisted columns are gradually transformed into a pair of fluted pillars. It is also interesting to trace the development of floral ornament before the second Baroque stage, characterised by the large and robust Torah breastplates of the second half of the nineteenth century, mostly of Viennese provenance. We find similar, if more muted, developments in the decoration of other silver from synagogues, such as the Torah finials, crowns, and Levite sets.

A fine filigree was used from the mid-eighteenth century for the decoration of pointers and spice boxes and other silver products. Two noteworthy examples are a cylindrical silver-gilt scroll case for the Book of Esther (cat. M129) and a Baroque silver filigree book binding with a silver clasp and a motif of blessing hands (cat. M128).

Objects made of tin and copper, and used for celebrations at home, reveal a rather different attitude to decoration. Here a more vernacular style and a naïve abstraction predominate and the decoration is closer to folk art. Of course, boundaries are not

M3 Breastplate with chain, silver, 1790

always clear-cut. The vernacular, for example, does not necessarily exclude the representational, as we can see from a pewter Passover plate of Joseph and Potiphar's wife (cat. M112).

BREASTPLATES (*Tassim*) are usually made of silver and hung with a silver chain on the Torah rollers so that they cover the upper part of the Torah mantle. In the lower third of the breastplate is an opening where labels with the names of Jewish holidays can be inserted (it is quite probable that the Torah breastplates evolved from this use of interchangeable labels). Pendants with the names of the donors are sometimes attached to the lower edge of the breastplate. Their shape, formerly rectangular and later a grooved cartouche, encouraged decoration and this was inspired by traditional Jewish motifs: the Torah crown, the Tables of the Law, two heraldic lions, as well as architecture. An example exhibited here is the silver chased breastplate from Prague, made in 1783 (cat. M1). Silver objects made in Prague or Vienna apparently differ in their formal approach from those made in Moravia. A breastplate from Western Moravia, dated 1790, has a decoration indicating a local and rustic stylisation (cat. M6). The most precious plates in the collection are the little ones (mostly unmarked) that are gilded and perforated or in repoussé, and decorated with floral ornaments with inserted animal or bird figures.

TORAH FINIALS (*Rimonim*) are placed on the upper part of the Torah rollers. They can be divided into three groups.

The majority of those in the Museum's collection are of the Ashkenazi type, with a round base and a pomegranate head. The Italian type, in which the trunk holds several balustrades with little bells attached, is less frequent. The collection does not include any examples of the third type, with a Gothic spire.

TORAH CROWNS (singular, *Keter*), like the finials, decorate the Torah though the two were rarely used together. When they were, a special open crown with a holder was used (cat. M26). The crown was not essential for the decoration of the Torah and many Jewish religious communities in Bohemia and Moravia did not even own one. The oldest crown in the collection was made in the workshop of a Prague master in the 1720s.

POINTERS (*Yadim*) are also part of the Torah decoration, and sometimes called 'little hands' because of their characteristic form. Their use protects the parchment scrolls of the Torah for it means that they are not touched by the hands of the readers. The pointers can take on various shapes: twisted or hollow, decorated with chasing or filigree, with a square or rectangular cross-section. The majority of pointers from the eighteenth century are made of solid silver. The later ones are more fragile. A silver-gilt pointer from the seventeenth century, decorated with a figure of a griffin and rich floral ornaments, is a rarity (cat. M60).

SPICE BOXES (*Hadasim l' besamim*) are used at home for private celebrations of the end of Sabbath. The spice boxes in the collection date mostly from the eighteenth and nineteenth centuries, and are usually in the form of Gothic or Baroque spires. The spire type lasted until the twentieth century when spice boxes in the form of blossoms and fruit were also being made. During the twentieth century, the traditional motifs were

M9 Breastplate with three pendants and chain,
silver, parcel-gilt, 1770

further enriched with new forms such as fish, musical instruments, or even steam locomotives (cat. M73, M75, M82), and there are curious examples of spice boxes shaped like a windmill and a kettle (cat. M72, M76).

Also related to the ceremony of the Sabbath is a pendant Sabbath lamp with light sources arranged like a star. They developed from antique lamps. The Museum owns twenty-six lamps of this type made of brass. They were mostly produced in Eastern Europe, some of them in Bohemia and Moravia.

The exhibition includes a selection of Kiddush cups. Such cups are among the oldest Jewish ritual objects, and are used for drinking wine on the return from the Sabbath-eve synagogue service. The majority of Kiddush cups were made of silver and have elaborate inscriptions of parts of, or the whole, Kiddush benediction.

After Kiddush comes the ritual washing of hands which precedes the breaking of bread and which is related to the ceremonial handwashing in the Temple prior to the priestly service. For this lavers and ewers are employed.

Also included in the exhibition are a number of *etrog* boxes used at the Festival of Tabernacles (*Sukkot*). The *etrog* is a kind of citrus fruit, and is protected in a special container which is sometimes formed like a large citron.

The Museum also has a collection of Ḥanukah lamps. These are used during the Ḥanukah festival, which is celebrated for eight days and so the lamps have eight main burners, one being lit each night until all eight are alight. The ninth burner, called a beadle light, is separate from the others, and is lit every night. The lights can take the form either of oval oil lamps or candlesticks. Ḥanukah lamps were produced in two versions – candelabra with eight or nine arms, and a bench type which derived from antique lamps.

Minor silver objects complete the collection of metalwork. They were used for various cult purposes. They include cleaning instruments and silver combs of the Burial Brotherhood (*Ḥevra Kadisha*), silver circumcision sets (cat. M155), several *mezuzot* (metal or wooden cases containing a particular passage from Deuteronomy, nailed to the door-post) and amulets (cat. M162).

M11 Breastplate with chain, silver, 1866–72

M12 Breastplate with chain and two pendants, silver, 1844(?)

M13 Breastplate with chain, silver, 1816

M14 Miniature breastplate, silver, 2nd half of
18th century

M22 Crown, silver, 1824

M36 One of a pair of *rimonim,* silver, 1815

M37 One of a pair of *rimonim,* silver, parcel-gilt, 1814

M47 Alms box, silver, 1781

M53 Alms box, silver, 1819

M55　Alms box, silver, 1813

M59　Pointer, silver

M65　Pointer, silver, c. end of 19th century

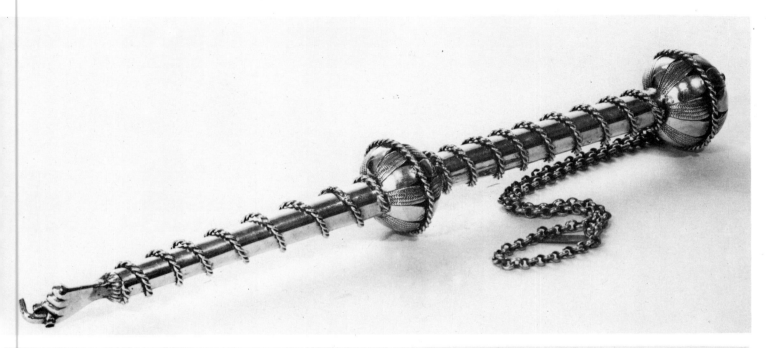

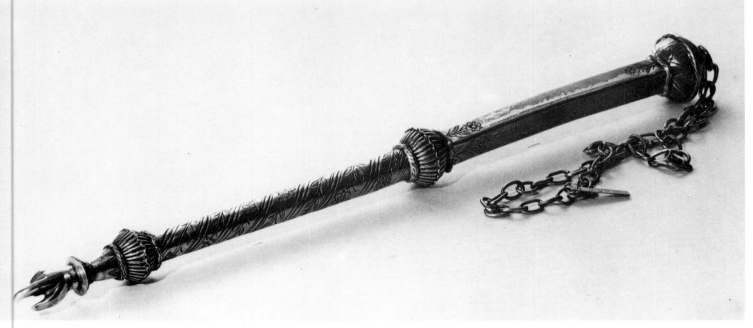

M73 Spice box, silver, 2nd half of 19th century

M75 Spice box, silver, parcel-gilt

169 Spice box, silver, 1844

M81 Spice box, silver, c.1850

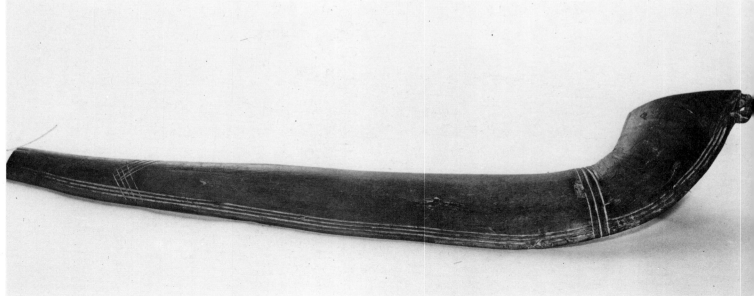

M99 Kiddush cup, silver, 1840

M103 Laver and ewer, silver, c.1870

M108 Passover plate, pewter, c. 1700

MI13 Passover plate, pewter, 1815

M115 *Etrog* box, silver, 1814

M116 *Etrog* box, silver, parcel-gilt, probably c.1675

M125 Charity box, wood, velvet and silver

M130 Comb and files, silver

M145 Hanukah lamp, brass, 18th century

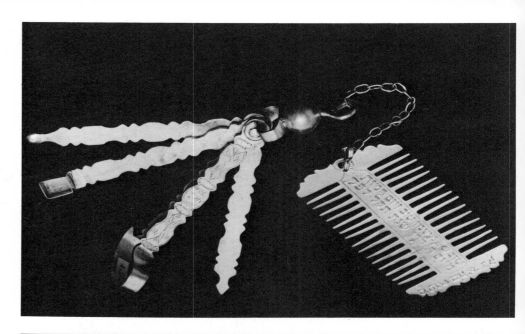

MI51 Sabbath lamp, brass, 1st half of 18th century

BREASTPLATES (TASSIM)

M1 Breastplate with three pendants
silver, repoussé and chased
Maker's mark: *J.F.* (J. Fourtner, d.1806),
Prague, 1783
31×23.8, 688 gm.
In the form of a niche, surmounted by a crown
and flanked by crowned and garlanded twisted
columns. The centre has a rectangular
opening, made to receive sliding,
interchangeable labels inscribed in Hebrew
with the names of different festivals. The
opening is within a Rococo border, on either
side of which is a flowering plant in a pot. The
lower panel of the breastplate bears a shell
within a scrolled cartouche and border.
Pendants inscribed in Hebrew with the name
of the donor, *Gershon, Slavkov, 1784.*
17.464

M2 Breastplate with three pendants and chain
silver, parcel-gilt, repoussé and chased
Maker's mark: *C.W.* (C. Wildt, 1761–1809),
1781
16×14, 300 gm.
In the form of a mantled breastplate,
surmounted by a coronet and flanked by
wreathed, twisted columns bearing coronets,
the whole within a Rococo border composed
of 'C' and 'S' scrolls. The central opening is
contained within a cartouche and is fitted with
a label and the plate is supported on a chased
plinth with a scrolled shell in the centre. The
pendants are miniature versions of the
breastplate.
1.871

M3 Breastplate with chain*
silver cast, repoussé and chased
Maker's mark: *J.S.,* Znojmo, 1790
27×22.2, 605 gm.
Square with indented top corners and small
semi-circle above with leaf border. Flanking
squat columns with floral decoration stand on
chased plinths and are surmounted by lions
rampant supporting an applied coronet. A
bowed ribbon suspends a central rectangular
plaque bearing a Hebrew inscription, and rests
on an oval wreath.
10.400

M4 Breastplate with three pendants and chain
silver, repoussé and chased
Maker's mark: *B.T.* and *C.W.,* Prague, Old
Town, 1762
24.5×21.2, 550 gm.
Within an arched, rectangular beaded frame,
flanking pier-forms support a beaded bulbous
crown and have shell decoration and 'C' scrolls
above and below. In the centre, a framed
opening is fitted to receive interchangeable
labels.
10.611

M5 Breastplate with chain
silver, repoussé and chased
Maker's mark: *C.S.,* Prague, 1810
27.5×21.5, 500 gm.
Surmounted by a crown supported by two
lions rampant standing on pilasters with a
single flute. The central opening has a beaded
frame and is below a garland of flowers and
swagged laurel wreaths; the lower panel bears
a shell within 'C' scrolls and has chased
decoration.
17.465

M6 Breastplate with chain and bells
silver, repoussé and chased
Maker's mark: *F.Z.,* West Moravia, 1790
27.8×22.4, 527 gm.
Square with smaller arched top and plain
border. Two pairs of flanking columns have
entwined laurel leaves. The outer pair are
surmounted by vases of flowers, the inner by
lions rampant supporting an applied coronet
from which are suspended two (originally
three) bells. Below the coronet is a plaque
framed by a laurel leaf border bearing a
Hebrew inscription.
10.405

M7 Breastplate with chain
silver, repoussé and chased
Maker's mark: *W.S.,* 1814
23.2×20.4, 530 gm.
Square with smaller arched top. Flanking
fluted pilasters with shell capitals stand on
rectangular bases and are surmounted by lions
rampant supporting an applied coronet. A
seven-branch candelabrum between two

rosettes stands over the central opening which
is fitted to accept interchangeable labels.
Below are the Tables of the Law, inscribed
with the Ten Commandments, which flank a
circular medallion inscribed in Hebrew.
Donor: Leib, son of Leib, Vlašim, 1814.
2.183

M8 Breastplate with chain
silver, parcel-gilt, repoussé and chased
Maker's mark: *J.B.* (J. Sam. Bechensteiner,
1713–81), Norimberk, 1700–1750
17×14, 225 gm.
Square with smaller arched top and heavy
moulded frame. Against a rusticated
background two columns with striated bases
and capitals are surmounted by two lions
rampant supporting an applied coronet, above
which is shell and scroll decoration. The
opening below, which can take
interchangeable labels, has a frame decorated
with 'C' and 'S' scrolls and contains a plaque
inscribed in Hebrew.
13.501

M9 Breastplate with three pendants and chain*
silver, parcel-gilt, repoussé and chased
Hallmark: 1770
36.2×30.8, 100 gm.
Within an elaborate border of 'C' and 'S'
scrolls two pairs of columns stand on
rectangular pedestals bearing single rosettes
and are entwined with roses (inner) and vines
(outer). They are surmounted by lions
rampant, rear regardant, supporting a bulbous,
beaded crown. Below the crown is a central
opening with a seaweed border above and
below which is shell and 'C'-scroll decoration.
Rococo pendants with Hebrew inscriptions
including date of donation, 1817.
37.594

M10 Breastplate with chain
Maker's mark: *A.M.* (A. Marouschek),
Prague, 1848
19.5×15, 315 gm.
Rectangular with ogival arched top and
inscribed in Hebrew around border. Two
neo-Classical vases support lions rampant,
bearing sprays of fruit and foliage, which flank

plain Tables of the Law and a rectangular opening. Below is grotesque foliage and a basket of fruit, and above a bulbous crown with ball and pineapple finial.
1.874

M11 Breastplate with chain*

silver, repoussé, cast and chased
Maker's mark: *J.E.*, 1866–72
25.8×24.4, 528 gm.
Within an ornate, cartouche-shaped border of 'C' and 'S' scrolls, plain flanking columns with acanthus-leaf capitals are surmounted by cast lions rampant, rear regardant, supporting a bulbous crown with ball finial. Below are the Tables of the Law engraved with the Ten Commandments and a rectangular opening made to receive interchangeable labels. A lower plaque with a floral border is inscribed in Hebrew.
37.917

M12 Breastplate with chain and two pendants*

silver, repoussé and chased
Maker's mark: *A.W.* (And. Weichesmüller), Vienna, 1844 (?)
32.5×25, 637 gm.
Square, beneath open canopy. Squat bulbous flanking columns on rectangular pedestals, each column with an entwining single leaf, surmounted by lions rampant supporting a bulbous crown with a ball finial. Below, plain Tables of the Law, with sprays of roses and sunflowers to either side, stand above the central, rectangular opening. Shield-shaped pendants are suspended from either corner of a lower panel.
9.717

M13 Breastplate with chain*

silver, repoussé and chased
Maker's mark: *F.K.*, Brno, 1816
27.7×20.2, 480 gm.
Rectangular with rounded triangular arch. A pair of squat columns support two-tailed lions rampant, rear regardant, which flank the Tables of the Law engraved with the Roman numerals I – X and a framed rectangular opening for interchangeable labels. Above is a bulbous crown with a ball and pineapple finial

and below a basket of fruit between pairs of grotesque 'C'-shaped snakes. Stylised foliage in the background.
12.243

M14 Miniature breastplate*

silver, repoussé and chased
Unmarked; probably 2nd half of 18th century
17×14, 260 gm.
Rectangular with curved corners and arched top. Columns with acanthus capitals, surmounted by crowns and inscribed above the base in Hebrew, flank an oval medallion inscribed in Hebrew, which is surrounded by strapwork and sea-shell frame. The sides have scroll and strapwork decoration.
Donors: Representatives of the New Synagogue (Třebíc), 1753.
10.998

M15 Breastplate with three pendants and chain

silver, repoussé and chased
Maker's mark: *I.F.B.*, Brno, 1820s.
20×14, 260 gm.
Rectangular with arched top and beaded border. Two small plinths with rosette and ribbon decoration support lions rampant, rear regardant, which carry rectangular opening with laurel-leaf border. Behind are two cornucopias; above, a crown with ball finial and below, scrollwork decoration. The three oval medallions have beaded borders and are inscribed in Hebrew.
Donor: Mendl Tsukr, 1845.
3.745

TORAH CROWNS (singular, KETER TORA)

M16 Crown

silver, repoussé and chased
Maker's mark: *E.B.*, Vienna, 1852
15×13, 394 gm.
Circlet with alternating round and diamond gem shapes on a chased diapered background, the six arches spring from applied double rosettes (one missing) and are edged with beading. Surmounted by a nut finial, below which is suspended a small bell.
Donor: David Josef Eisler, 1861.
7.158

M17 Crown

silver, repoussé and applied
Maker's mark: *A.W.*, Vienna, 1834
19.8×16, 550 gm.
Circlet embossed with jewel shapes, the six arches have beaded borders and applied ornament. Surmounted by a smaller, similar crown with a nut finial, within which is suspended a bell with a border decorated with sea shells.
Donor: David Josef Eisler, 1861.
12.196

M18 Crown

silver, repoussé and chased
Maker's mark: *T.R.*, Vienna, 1853
27.5×24, 960 gm.
On a circlet decorated with alternating embossed gem shapes and applied foliate scrolls, six swelling arches with applied ornament are interspersed with six foreshortened pierced trefoils embossed with flowers, foliage and scrolls. Surmounted by a similar, smaller crown with a plain ovoid finial, below which is suspended a bell.
12.292

M19 Crown

silver, repoussé, chased and engraved
Maker's mark: *T.R.*, Vienna, 1847
15.5×11.4, 2025 gm.
On a circlet decorated with embossed gem shapes alternating with chased stylised flowers, the six arches have similar chased decoration. Finial in the form of a small engraved crown with flattened arches and a high base, below which is suspended a bell.
4.230

M20 Crown

silver, repoussé and chased
Maker's mark: *F.K.*, 1818
15×13.7, 685 gm.
Circlet decorated with applied imitation jewels and silver flowers. Each of the six arches has a beaded border and springs from a rosette inset with an artificial jewel, above which another stone is set in applied foliage. Ball finial resting in acanthus and laurel leaves, below which is suspended a bell.
104.765

M21 Crown

silver, repoussé, chased and engraved
Maker's mark: *T.D.*, 1866–72
27.5×22, 1010 gm.
Circlet with beaded border, decorated with alternating embossed diamond and oval gem shapes, between which runs a Hebrew inscription. Six Rococo arches embossed with roses and palm leaves within scroll borders are surmounted by a miniature crown finial with a bell.
Donor: Sarga Feiveš, 1886.
1.592

M22 Crown*

silver, repoussé and chased
Maker's mark: *F.K.*, 1824
40×33, 2250 gm.
Circlet with applied gem shapes, rosettes and cinquefoils on granulated background. Six arches with beaded borders and applied rosettes, surmounted by finial in the form of an eagle on a pierced base with applied rosettes.
3.674

M23 Crown

silver, parcel-gilt, repoussé and engraved; semi-precious stones
Maker's mark: *A.K.* (A. Kohl), Vienna, 1830–72
43×24.5, 1940 gm.
Plain circlet set with semi-precious stones and inscribed on the lower edge in Hebrew. Six arches with embossed scrolls and foliage and chased trellis pattern, surmounted by smaller similar crown with ball finial.
44.314

M24 Crown*

silver, parcel-gilt, repoussé and engraved
Maker's mark: *H.S.* (?), 1900
30×25, 1383 gm.
Circlet embossed with alternating diamond and oval gem shapes on a stippled background and with a panel bearing a three-line inscription. Six arches spring from coronet of alternating flower heads and trefoils raised on pierced points and are embossed with flower and foliage motifs within scroll borders, each

arch joined to the next by a floral ornament from which a bell is suspended. Surmounted by a smaller crown with a ball finial and containing a bell.
10.444

M25 Crown

silver, repoussé, pierced and engraved
Unmarked; inscription includes date, February 1905
29×24.5, 1055 gm.
Circlet inscribed in German above and below a beaded centre. Elaborate, eight-arched top in pseudo-Rococo style from which are suspended eight bells. Finial in the form of a double fluted cone.
37.443

M26 Crown

silver, parcel-gilt, pierced and engraved
Unmarked
21.5×17.5, 787 gm.
Circlet of pierced and embossed ornament bordering a German inscription, surmounted by six panels decorated with pierced rose bushes. Two small pierced arches support a bulbous crown finial.
2.166

M27 Crown

silver, parcel-gilt and repoussé
Maker's mark: *G.K.* (George Kahlert the younger 1732–72)
32.5×15.5, 1270 gm.
Circlet decorated with shells, scrolls and beads surmounted by a band of Rococo ornament from which spring six arches with embossed decoration, supporting a small crown with a pineapple finial.
5.332

M28 Crown

silver, repoussé and chased
Maker's mark: Vienna, 1830–39 (?)
11.8×24, 640 gm.
Circlet with repoussé imitation jewels and bead border from which spring six arches with applied ornament. The smaller similar crown which surmounts them has a ball finial.
10.380

M29 Crown

silver, repoussé and chased
Unmarked; Bohemia, c.2nd half of 19th century
39×21.7, 1960 gm.
Circlet with alternating flowers and repoussé imitation jewels on chased background with applied plaque bearing German inscription. Eight arches elaborately embossed with flowery foliage and scrolls, connected to one another by further foliate ornaments from which are suspended bells. Surmounted by small crown with flower finial and containing a bell.
37.486

M30 Crown

silver, parcel-gilt and repoussé
Maker's mark: *A.W.*, Vienna, 1845
30×29, 1243 gm.
Circlet in two parts with beaded borders enclosing roundels, and connected by two large palm leaves. Six plain arches with applied decoration spring from scroll and foliage ornamentation and bear a plain crown with acanthus finial and containing a bell.
7.396

M31 Crown colour plate VII

silver, parcel-gilt and repoussé; semi-precious stones 1913
28.5×23, 2700 gm.
Formed as an Imperial Habsburg crown. Circlet with beaded borders, above which are acanthus leaves and scrolling. The upper crown, in three sections with beaded borders, supports an orb with a ball finial. The whole inset with imitation jewels and semi-precious stones.
17.561

M32 Crown

silver, parcel-gilt, repoussé and chased
Maker's mark: *J.E.*, 1862
22×17.3, 852 gm.
The circlet, decorated with diamond shapes and acanthus leaves between two bands of beading, supports a pierced tier of foliage and beads which is surmounted by eight arches decorated with sunflowers on a chased background. In the centre hangs a small bell

and the whole is surmounted by a finial with roses.
Donor: Ruben Heller.
1.172

TORAH FINIALS (RIMONIM)

M33 Pair of rimonim
silver, parcel-gilt
Maker's mark: *R.F.* (Richard Fleischmann), Prague, Mala Strana (?), 1783 (?)
44×17.9, 3260 gm.
Each has a base with a Hebrew inscription on the rim, naming the donor, decorated with beading, festoons of fruit and vases. The fluted stem supports two balustraded galleries from which hang balls, the upper gallery supporting four balusters. On these stands a vase with drapery festoons.
Donor: Wolf, son of Azriel Gadls, 1784.
46.002 a, b

M34 Pair of rimonim
silver, repoussé and chased
Maker's mark: *C.S.,* Prague, 1813
40.6×14.5, 1320 gm.
The tiered circular base, decorated with vine leaves, supports a baluster stem ornamented with flowers and strapwork and, at the top, beading and foliage, into which is set a Habsburg crown decorated with bead work, with a ball finial.
17.501 a, b

M35 Pair of rimonim
silver, parcel-gilt
Maker's mark: *A.M.,* 1839
31.7×7.6, 1153 gm.
The lower part of each shaft, whose rim is delicately chased, is decorated with a band of flowers and bends out to form six leaves from which are suspended bells. The upper part of the shaft which fits into this is surmounted by a Habsburg crown whose rim is decorated with flowers, beading and foliate ornament, and the bulbous body with beading and a ball finial.
10.861 a, b

M36 Pair of rimonim*
silver, repoussé
Maker's mark: *A.N.* (Ant. Nowak), Prague, 1815
40×15, 908 gm.
The circular base decorated with embossed foliage, supports a baluster shaft divided into three tiers, each decorated with panels of various flowers. The rim of the circular base of the third tier is ornamented with two borders of beading outside embossed foliage. The third tier leads into a crown of six arches with a pineapple finial.
17.528 a, b

M37 Pair of rimonim*
silver, parcel-gilt
Maker's mark: *C.S.* (Carl Skremenec), Prague, 1814
34.3×10.6, 796 gm.
Each takes the form of a baluster-shaped column, chased with flower, scroll and foliage ornament, supported on a circular base and topped by a crown mounted in embossed foliage with beading around the circlet and over the surface. A small ball finial at the top.
1.524 a, b

M38 Pair of rimonim
silver, repoussé and chased
Maker's mark: *T.H.* (T. Höpfel active 1815–1847), Prague, 1821
39×15.8, 1485 gm.
Each has a double baluster stem decorated with cartouches containing flowers and foliage, supported on a bulbous base similarly ornamented. The whole is surmounted by a crown with a ball finial, set within overlapping fruit and foliage and containing a small bell.
1.653 a, b

M39 Pair of rimonim
silver, repoussé and chased
Maker's mark: *G.S.* (G. Schumacher), Vienna 1866
32.5×11.3, 1090 gm.
The base and baluster stem are decorated at intervals with bands of flowers and 'C' scrolls, and support a bulbous body ornamented with bunches of roses in a plain irregular framework. From this are suspended six bells and a further six from an inverted plate above. The whole is surmounted by a crown with a large ball finial.
2.513 a, b

M40 Pair of rimonim
silver, chased
Maker's mark: *A.N.* (A. Nodin), Prague, 1820
34×9.7, 1055 gm.
The plain domed base and tubular stem support a crown decorated with beading and chased acanthus foliage on the circlet, and containing a small bell. A double-eagle finial above.
7.108 a, b

M41 Pair of rimonim
silver, repoussé and chased
Maker's mark: *C.S.* (Carl Skremenec), Prague, 1810
37×14.4, 1342 gm.
The shaft, decorated with two chased bands and with a chased knop, on a spreading circular chased base, supports a crown with beaded and 'C'-scroll decoration, which contains a small bell.
10.639 a, b

M42 Pair of rimonim
silver, repoussé and chased
Maker's mark: *I.R.,* Prague, 1792
38.5×10.5, 685 gm.
Baluster stem on shaped base with sea shell and laurel-leaf decoration, surmounted by a Habsburg crown with 'C'-scroll decoration above the circlet and with a pineapple finial, the crown containing a bell.
Donor: Yehuda Leb, Polná, 1796.
1.916 a, b

M43 Pair of rimonim
silver, parcel-gilt, repoussé and chased
Maker's mark: *M.E.* (M. Entzinger 1740–90), Prague, 1769
43.3×11.5, 1920 gm.
A double-baluster stem on a shaped base with 'C' scroll, shell and floral decoration in irregular cartouches. The rim of the base has chased floral decoration and bears a Hebrew inscription. The stem is surmounted by a

Habsburg crown, pierced, with a ball finial, and containing a bell.
Donors: The representatives of Velkodvorská Synagogue, 1770.
37.571 a, b

M44 Pair of rimonim
silver, parcel-gilt, repoussé and chased
Maker's mark: *A.K.,* 1817
42.4×17.8, 2170 gm.
A baluster stem, decorated with repoussé foliage around the knop, on a shaped base with repoussé vine-leaf and floral ornament, the base rim bearing a Hebrew inscription, supports a Habsburg crown, with circlet of foliage and beading and a pineapple finial, containing a bell.
Donors: Wolf Radisch, Wolf Flekeles and Meir Wilhartitz, 1817.
35.570 a, b

M45 Pair of rimonim
silver, parcel-gilt, repoussé and chased
Maker's mark: *M.E.* (M. Entzinger 1740–90), Prague, Old Town
43.5×17.7, 1758 gm.
A double-baluster stem on a shaped base, with 'C'-scroll and floral decoration in irregular cartouches, on a base whose rim bears a Hebrew inscription. The stem is surmounted by a Habsburg crown, set in foliage and pierced with a ball finial, and containing a bell.
Donor: Abraham, son of Efraim Obner, 1768.
37.572 a, b

M46 Pair of rimonim
silver, parcel-gilt, chased
Maker's mark: *C.S.,* Prague, 1815
36×14.8, 1234 gm.
The baluster stem chased with 'C'-scroll and floral decoration, stands on a similarly chased circular base with a Hebrew inscription around the rim, and supports a crown set in applied foliage, with a spike finial and containing a bell.
Donors: Yakob Eliyahu Šváb, Heřmanův Městec, 1844.
10.513 a, b

ALMS BOXES

M47 Alms box*
silver, repoussé and chased
Maker's mark: *T.S.,* 1781
13.5×8, 300 gm.
Cylindrical tankard on raised base with repoussé foliage on chased ground, the Hebrew inscription on plain ground bordered with chased flowers and foliage. The hinged domed lid has a border of repoussé foliage on chased ground and a raised slot. 'S'-scroll handle at the side.
Donors: Mordechai, son of R. J., Tsevi Hirsch Segal, Leb, the Representatives of *Hevra Kadisha,* 1781.
7.042

M48 Alms box
silver, engraved
Maker's mark: *C.K.,* 1815 (?)
12.8×9, 222 gm.
A cylindrical container engraved with flowering plants, on the cover is mounted an engraved slot, and at the side a semi-circular handle.
4.479

M49 Alms box
silver, chased
Maker's mark: *A.F.,* Jihlava, 1849
16.5×14.3, 675 gm.
Cylindrical body with bands of chased decoration, domed lid with chased rim and hinged fastening and bearing a raised slot, 'S'-scroll handle.
1.920

M50 Alms box
silver, engraved
Maker's mark: *E.S.* (Emer Scheinest), Vienna, 1851
13.5×9, 260 gm.
In the form of a plain jug with a central band of flowers, shells and scrolls, the hinged tin lid bearing a raised slot, and a scroll handle at the side.
3.656

M51 Alms box
silver, repoussé and chased
Maker's mark: *E.M.,* Brno, 1836
16.3×14.3, 570 gm.
In the shape of a tankard with two encircling bands of repoussé vine and gem-form decoration with a medallion below the clasp bearing an engraved Hebrew inscription, a further inscription around the base. The hinged and domed lid bears a raised slot and the handle is in the form of an 'S'-scroll.
10.346

M52 Alms box
silver, repoussé and chased
Unmarked; 1786
15.6×10.4, 510 gm.
Cylindrical body on raised base, decorated with flowers and festoons of foliage. Two chased Hebrew inscriptions within 'C'-scroll borders, the hinged lid bearing the year in Hebrew on the large raised slot. Two 'S'-scroll handles.
23.035

M53 Alms box*
silver, chased
Maker's mark: Vienna, 1819
16.5×7, 520 gm.
The rectangular container bears chased decoration at the edges and a Hebrew inscription below the hinged clasp of the cover. Further inscriptions appear on the domed rectangular lid which bears a raised slot. Angular handle.
Donors: Yehoshua Ber, son of Aharon; Chayim, son of Leb Telč Tsahlfan; Yakov, son of Shelomo Tsoref Pehem; Nachum, son of Eliakum Glaiser, the Representatives of *Hevra Kadisha,* 1819.
3.797

M54 Alms box
silver, chased
Maker's mark: *T.K.,* Brno, 1810
17×8, 440 gm.
Plain cylindrical body with Hebrew inscription around the base and centre and two bands of leaf and stem decoration. The hemispherical cover is hinged and has a hinged clasp, and bears further leaf ornament and a

large raised slot. The handle is shaped as an 'S'-scroll.
Donors: Shelomo Ber, Shimon H"B, Abraham Breml, the Representatives of *Hevra Kadisha*, 1812.
4.267

M55 Alms box*
silver, repoussé and chased
Maker's mark: *T.F.*; hallmark: Prague, 1813
18×12.6, 650 gm.
Plain cylindrical body on low base bearing two shields bordered by foliage decoration and containing Hebrew inscriptions. The domed lid with hinged clasp is bordered with repoussé ornament and bears a raised slot with scalloped edges. Two scroll handles.
2.174

POINTERS (YADIM)

M56 Pointer
silver, engraved
Hallmark: 1806–7
30, 157 gm.
The shaft is decorated with strapwork and entwining flowers and foliage, and divided by a knop with chased ornament. At one end a ball finial, ring and chain, at the other a hand with pointing finger.
3.962

M57 Pointer
silver, repoussé
Maker's mark: *A.D.*, 1819
24, 107 gm.
The tapering shaft, decorated with a continuous spiral band, is divided by a knop decorated with repoussé leaves. A similar ball at one end with ring and chain, at the other a hand with curved pointing finger.
10.455

M58 Pointer
silver, repoussé and chased
Maker's mark: *R.F.*, 1806–7
27.3, 140 gm.
The shaft, decorated with a spiral band interlaced with flowers and foliage, is in two

sections divided by a fluted knop, a similar finial with ring and chain at one end and hand with pointing finger at other.
37.402

M59 Pointer*
silver
Unmarked
27.5, 125 gm.
The shaft, with pointing hand at one end is decorated with an applied spiral-twisted chain, and is divided by a knop, formed in two halves of alternate plain and chased petals. The ball finial is of a similar construction and bears a ring and chain.
23.113

M60 Pointer
silver, parcel-gilt, cast and chased
Unmarked; c.1600–50
12.8, 35 gm.
The shaft is decorated with a continuous spiral of flowers and foliage leading to a capital of scrolls and foliage which supports a finial of a griffin and the chain. At the other end, a hand with pointing finger.
32.131

M61 Pointer
silver and ivory, chased
Marked; Bohemia, 18th century (?)
19.5, 55 gm.
The hand and central section with plain knop are of silver, and are divided by a carved ivory section. The upper part of the shaft is also of carved ivory, and the chain is attached to a ring passing through a hole in the handle. At the other end a pointing hand.
173.697

M62 Pointer
silver, chased
c.1820
30.2, 80 gm.
The shaft is in two sections, divided by a plain knop. The lower part leading to the pointing hand is formed of a spiral-twisted strap, the upper part is a tapering rectangular handle chased with Hebrew inscription. A ball finial bears a large ring and chain.
4.463

M63 Pointer
silver, repoussé
c.1806–7
31.8, 207 gm.
The plain tapering four-sided shaft, leading to a cuff and pointing hand is surmounted by applied palm leaves and repoussé knop. The pierced handle is surmounted by a flattened knob with ring and chain.
44.178

M64 Pointer
silver, engraved
Maker's mark: *C.S.*, Prague, 1819
26.4, 120 gm.
The shaft is in two sections with a plain knop, the lower part leading to the pointing hand in the form of spiralling strap, the handle rectangular with an engraved Hebrew inscription, surmounted by a ball finial with large ring and chain.
37.497

M65 Pointer*
silver, repoussé and engraved
c. end of 19th century
29, 120 gm.
The shaft is in two sections, the lower cylindrical part engraved with spiral and flower and foliage ornament, at the end a fluted knop and pointing hand. A similar knop divides the lower shaft from the plain rectangular handle, each side of which is engraved with a plant, and is surmounted by a chased knop-like finial bearing a ring and chain.
846

M66 Pointer
silver, chased
Maker's mark: *A.F.*, 1821
25.6, 127 gm.
The shaft is divided into two sections by a plain knop; the lower section conical with an engraved and chased spiral band leading to a cuff and pointing hand, the handle rectangular with chamfered angles and engraved Hebrew inscriptions, surmounted by a ball finial with ring and chain.
4.409

M67 Pointer
silver, repoussé and chased
Maker's mark: *P.S.*, Vienna, 1830–50
19, 120 gm.
The plain baluster shaft is intersected by two mouldings of scroll and shell decoration and the centre section is engraved with a Hebrew inscription. The mouldings are repeated at either end, one leading to a pointing hand, the other to a finial with large ring and chain.
17.543

SPICE BOXES (HADASIM L' BESAMIM)

M68 Spice box
silver, filigree
Hallmark: Brno, 1861
20×6.1, 103 gm.
The body, in the form of a square tower with a spire, is carried on a sprung support with a square base and four bun feet. Flags fly from five pinnacles. One side of the tower contains a door.
37.984

M69 Spice box*
silver, filigree
Maker's mark; *Loeb Jakob Wien,* Prague, 1844
14.5, 40 gm.
The body consists of two hemispherical bowls with a solid band between. The upper bowl hinged to form a lid and surmounted by a flag. The body is supported by a twisted-wire tripod on a ring base.
174.372

M70 Spice box
silver, filigree
2nd half of 18th century
26.5, 306 gm.
The body in the form of a two-tiered hexagonal tower is supported on a galleried platform on a knopped stem. The hexagonal base has claw and ball feet at the corners. The tower is surmounted by an onion-domed cupola and a flag. The pinnacles of the lower tier also have flags.
173.696

M71 Spice box
silver
Vienna, c.1840
13, 10 gm.
Pierced and fluted fruit-shaped burner supported by a stem bearing a serpent on an elaborate foliate base. The hinged lid in the form of a rosette.
12.744

M72 Spice box
silver
2nd half of 19th century
7.5, 30 gm.
Shaped as a kettle (?) chased with animals and birds and supported on a tripod formed of three serpents. The hinged top surmounted by a small cast bird.
3.988

M73 Spice box*
silver, filigree
2nd half of 19th century
5×4.5, 25 gm.
Shaped as a locomotive engine with filigree body, two funnels, and with a hinged cover at the front with 'S'-scroll handle.
3.964

M74 Spice box
silver, filigree
Maker's mark: *A.K.*, 1843
20×15, 200 gm.
Octagonal casket supported by four hemispherical feet, and ornamented with a large rosette on the top of the rectangular lid. Smaller rosettes surmount the upper corners of the main body and the lid.
174.178

M75 Spice box*
silver, parcel-gilt and filigree
Unmarked
9×3.4, 20 gm.
Shaped as a six-stringed mandolin with hinged back in the form of a rosette.
173.841

M76 Spice box
silver, pierced
Maker's mark; c. 1st half of 19th century (?)
5, 12 gm.
In the form of a windmill with four vanes. Octagonal turret on a circular base with four ball feet surmounted by a finial bearing a flag.
173.395

M77 Spice box
silver, pierced
Unmarked; turret and spire c. 2nd half of 18th century, stem c. early 19th century
16.3×6, 142 gm.
Square turret with a flag at each upper corner supported by a baluster stem on a circular foot on a square base, surmounted by a four-sided spire with a finial bearing a flag.
173.122

M78 Spice box
silver, filigree
Unmarked; c. 1880
3.2×2.2, 20 gm.
Formed as a plain circular box, the lid ornamented with a filigree rosette. The underside engraved with a Latin dedication.
4.369

M79 Spice box
silver, filigree
Unmarked; c.1810
19, 90 gm.
Cylindrical body with curved top surmounted by a ball and flag finial and supported by a tripod with a knop on a ring base.
10.695

M80 Spice box
silver, filigree
Unmarked; c.1900
8.5×4, 40 gm.
Oval box with lid divided into two hinged parts, the whole with filigree ornament.
3.969

M81 Spice box*
silver, filigree
Unmarked; c.1850
7.2×7.7, 44 gm.
In the shape of a locomotive engine, the

cylindrical boiler having filigree ornament and a hinged cover at the end. (See cat. M73).
173.982

M82 Spice box*
silver
Unmarked; probably end of 19th century
13.8, 65 gm.
Shaped as a fish with overlapping scales to form articulated body. The hinged head has eyes of red glass. The mouth also opens and is hinged.
174.310

RAM'S HORNS (SHOFAROT)

M83 Shofar*
Ram's horn, engraved
45
61.292/2

M84 Shofar
Ram's horn
27
32.854/3

M85 Shofar
Ram's horn
38
12.047/1

M86 Shofar
Ram's horn
29
57.259

M87 Shofar
Ram's horn
32
68.936/2

M88 Shofar
Ram's horn
37
28.202

M89 Shofar
Ram's horn
32
32.854/2

KIDDUSH CUPS

M90 Kiddush cup
silver
Maker's mark: *M.J.*, after 1866
5.8×6.8, 45 gm.
Beaker with engraved decoration (including buildings and plants) and Hebrew inscription at base. One of a set of eight with similar decoration. (See also cat. M101)
173.049

M91 Kiddush cup
silver, chased
Maker's mark: *A.V.*, end of 19th century
11.1×7.6, 87 gm.
The cup, resting on a circular stepped foot, is decorated with a medallion bearing a Hebrew inscription and flanked by bunches of grapes, with horizontal bands of wave decoration around the rim and base.
1.178

M92 Kiddush cup
silver
Unmarked; c.1860
15.5×9.2, 408 gm.
The cup, its lower part lobed, resting on a short stem and circular lobed base, decorated with eight engraved cartouches and scrolls.
4.161

M93 Kiddush cup
silver, parcel-gilt
Maker's mark: *A.V.*, c.1866–68
12×8.5, 150 gm.
The cup, with lobed bowl, rests on a stem and stepped base, gadrooned, and is engraved with a Hebrew inscription.
12.157

M94 Kiddush cup
silver, parcel-gilt
Maker's mark: *T.D.* (T. Dub), 1866–72
11.5×9.5, 308 gm.
Cup with engraved Hebrew inscription supported by stem and circular base decorated with bands of embossed and engraved scroll ornament.
3.747

M95 Kiddush cup
silver, parcel-gilt, cast, applied and chased
1872
17.8×9.7, 165 gm.
The plain cup, with engraved Hebrew inscription, is set in a lobed bowl decorated with applied and chased grapes and vine leaves on the short, lobed, baluster stem. The round base with wave-shaped rim is decorated with alternating plain gadroons and applied grape and vine-leaf ornament.
4.372

M96 Kiddush cup
silver, parcel-gilt
Maker's mark: *M.G.*, 1907
21.5×9, 225 gm.
The cup with engraved German and Hebrew inscriptions within cartouches of 'C'-scrolls is supported on a baluster stem with beading on a circular raised base with embossed foliage border.
37.451 a

M97 Kiddush cup
silver, repoussé
Maker's mark: *A.N.*, 1875
18.5×7.5, 145 gm.
Cup engraved with Hebrew and German inscriptions and decorated with engraved foliage supported on baluster and fluted stem with two ornamented knops on circular base with embossed decoration.
Donor: R. Yom Tov Tsevi, 1876.
37.397

M98 Kiddush cup*
silver, parcel-gilt, repoussé, applied and chased
Maker's mark: after 1872
20.7×8.6, 267 gm.
The plain cup with Hebrew inscription is set in a bowl of cast and chased foliage and rests on a baluster stem, reeded, with a knop of chased and applied foliage, on a circular base with overlapping applied and chased leaves.
Donor: Town of Nymburk, 1891
17.875

M99 Kiddush cup*
silver, repoussé and chased
Maker's mark: *L.F.,* 1840
14.2×9.4, 188 gm.
Cup with swelling bowl, decorated with
chased vines and embossed flower, foliage and
scroll ornament, supported by a round,
wave-edged, base with a band of repoussé
ornament.
44.301

M100 Kiddush cup
silver, parcel-gilt
Unmarked
23.8×8.8
Plain cup held within a bowl of pierced scroll
foliate decoration with angels' heads,
supported on stem resting on tiered circular
base with scroll ornament.
17.556

M101 Seven Kiddush cups
silver, parcel-gilt
Each: 4.5×3.2, 8 gm.
Seven beakers from the same set as M90.
10.337/1–7

LAVERS AND EWERS

M102 Laver and ewer
silver
Maker's mark: *C.S.,* Prague, 1818
Laver: 40×28, 615 gm.
Ewer: 25.3×14.5, 440 gm.
Oval laver with plain well and the rim chased
with fleurs-de-lys. Ewer, with cast scroll
handle, bears a Hebrew inscription and is
chased with foliate decoration, supported by a
stem with a compressed knop on a circular
foot.
Donor: Anshil Tausik, 1819.
17.549 a, b

M103 Laver and ewer*
silver
Unmarked; c.1870
Laver: 12.6×23.7, 607 gm.
Ewer: 38×29, 965 gm.
The laver is deep and plain with two raised

sides. The ewer has a plain body with a cast
handle and is supported on a rectangular base.
7.225 a, b

M104 Laver and ewer
silver, chased
Unmarked; c.1870
Laver: 12.6×23.7, 607 gm.
Ewer: 38×29, 965 gm.
The laver has a deep plain well, the sides and
rim chased with volute scroll decoration and a
Hebrew inscription within a cartouche. The
ewer has an inverted pear-shaped body with
similar chased scroll decoration and Hebrew
inscription and rests on a stem on a stepped
circular base with a further inscription. The
handle is in the form of an 'S'-scroll.
Donor: Dr Tsevi Hirsch, 1871.
2.252 a, b

M105 Laver and ewer
silver, chased
Maker's mark: *K.M.,* 1845
Laver: 24.4, 735 gm.
Ewer: 32.8×20.9, 720 gm.
The laver has a deep rectangular plain well
with Hebrew inscription on the bottom. The
ewer, with an engraved Hebrew inscription
around the bulbous base of the body, stands on
a raised circular base, and has an 'S'-scroll
handle.
32.419

SILVER DISHES

These may have been used for the
Circumcision ceremony or for the ceremony
of the Redemption of the First-born.

M106 Dish
silver, repoussé and chased
c.1850
31×24, 501 gm.
An oval dish with a scalloped rim decorated
with flowers and foliage, the centre depicting
the Parting of the Red Sea in relief.
170.749

M107 Dish colour plate VI
silver, repoussé and chased
c.1850
23.5×33.5
An oval dish with a wide rim decorated with
repoussé beading and the signs of the Zodiac.
The centre of the dish depicts the Sacrifice of
Isaac in relief.
32.132

PEWTER PASSOVER AND MARRIAGE PLATES

M108 Passover plate*
pewter, chased
Saxony, c.1700
35.5, 1370 gm.
The wide rim is chased with Hebrew words
from the Passover service within laurel-leaf
medallions. The bottom is decorated with the
figure of a man in a hat, the Paschal lamb, a
goblet, flowers, and Hebrew words contained
in six-pointed stars within circles.
173.777

M109 Passover plate
pewter, chased
Maker's mark: *J.G.* (Josef Künzel), Plzeň, 1803
29, 853 gm.
The rim is chased with a Hebrew inscription
and the bottom depicts a scene of seven people
celebrating Passover with an attendant.
3.768

M110 Plate
pewter, chased
Maker's mark: *J.G.* (Josef Künzel), Plzeň, 1803
29, 883 gm.
The rim is chased with a Hebrew inscription,
and the inside with a further inscription and a
crown and tulips.
Donor: Golčův Jeníkov, 1830.
49.422

M111 Plate
pewter, chased
Maker's mark: *J.P.* (Josef Pitroff), Karlovy
Vary, end of 18th century
28.7, 896 gm.
The outer rim is chased with a Hebrew

inscription and inside a further inscription encircles a flower with six petals between which are small tulips and roses.
Donors: Association of Young Men, Popelka, 1842.
173.821

M112 Passover plate
pewter, engraved
Illegible mark; 1815
28, 820 gm.
The rim is decorated with spiral border, a Hebrew inscription and a rosette. Inside, a border of foliage encircles a representation of Joseph and Potiphar's wife.
37.696

M113 Passover plate*
pewter, engraved
Illegible maker's mark; 1815
33, 920 gm.
The rim bears a Hebrew inscription with small trees between the words. The bottom of the plate contains low roundels with Hebrew words indicating the Paschal ritual, a stylised horse, and the date.
173.825

ETROG BOXES

M114 Etrog box
silver, repoussé, parcel-gilt
Maker's mark: *W.B.,* end of 19th century
17.8×6, 130 gm.
Oval container with irregular rim and repoussé leaf ornament, and irregularly scalloped base.
904

M115 Etrog box*
silver, engraved
Maker's mark: *S.J.*; hallmark: Vienna, 1814
8.5×9.2, 128 gm.
Oval container, decorated with interlocking open geometric ornament, slightly domed cover with an ornamental border and rosette finial. At each end, serpentine handles.
3.785

M116 Etrog box*
silver wine-taster, parcel-gilt, repoussé, probably used as an *etrog* box
Maker's mark: *E.B.,* Augsburg, probably c.1675
14.5×16, 131 gm.
Oval six-lobed container, with embossed fruit and vine leaves in the centre surrounded by beaded border. Two cast 'S'-scroll handles.
173.826

M117 Etrog box
silver, parcel-gilt, repoussé, chased and pierced
Maker's mark: *N.M.,* c.1855
18.5×11.5, 110 gm.
Oval container on plain oval base, pierced fluted sides in the form of foliage with irregularly shaped rim, a Hebrew inscription around the centre.
2.205

M118 Etrog box
silver, pierced and chased
Unmarked; 1822
12.4×19.7, 370 gm.
The pierced oval body is formed of foliage and rests on an oval stepped base, the upper part of which is decorated with palm-leaf scrolls, the rims with a Hebrew inscription.
Donors: Miriam, widow of Moshe Zekeles; Kizl, wife of R. Wolf Rašic, 1822.
37.567

M119 Etrog box
silver, repoussé and chased
Maker's mark: *C.S.,* 1820
9.3×14.6, 250 gm.
Bulbous oval container, the cover chased with scroll decoration and a Hebrew inscription, in the centre a citron finial.
37.566

M120 Etrog box
silver,
13×15.5, 400 gm.
Oval plain container on four raised ball and claw feet with cover engraved with Hebrew inscription and with embossed citron and foliage finial.
Donor: Jechezkiel Preseles, 1863.
46.042

JUG AND MUG OF ḤEVRA KADISHA

M121 Jug colour plate VIII, b
pottery
Mikulov, 1836
38.7×17
Decorated with a depiction of a burial scene, and Hebrew inscriptions around the bulbous base and the neck.
Donors: Mendl Jidls; Abraham Yitzhak Pilim, Mosche Leb Bizenc; Yechezkiel M''S.
8.048

M122 Mug colour plate VIII, a
Bohemian glass
Prague, 1783/84
18.5×13.7
Cylindrical body with painted burial scene and Hebrew inscription, and 'S'-scroll handle.
63.620

CHARITY BOXES

M123 Charity box
silver
Maker's mark: *I.W.* (Jos. Warenberg 1830–50)
11.9×3, 110 gm.
In the form of a deep circular dish with a candleholder and handle on opposite sides of the rim. Around the rim is a chased Hebrew inscription.
Donors: Shelomo Hirsch Klein; Pinchas Gold; Wolf Gros; Gabriel Kulka; 1835.
2.928

M124 Charity box
silver
Maker's mark: *A.N.* (Anton Neubert 1810–54)
22.5×2.8, 462 gm.
The box is in the form of a deep, wide-lipped dish divided inside into four sections and with a candleholder and a handle shaped as an acanthus leaf. The rim is chased with a decorative border and a Hebrew inscription.
Donor: Zacharja Gerscheles, 1813.
27.804

M125 Charity box*
wood, velvet and silver
Unmarked
18×14, 180 gm.
The cylindrical box is made of wood covered with brown velvet and is overlaid at top and bottom with repoussé silver borders, the upper chased with a Hebrew inscription, and with silver panels containing chased Hebrew inscriptions within an ornate framework of 'S'-scrolls, foliage and shells.
Donors: Zelke, son of Hirsch Abliz; Leib; Meir Bla Aharan M"S Sgl.
4.526

M126 Charity box
silver, engraved
Maker's mark: *AN* (Ant. Neubert 1810–54)
12.5×1.8, 141 gm.
In the form of a circular rimmed dish, divided in three sections with an engraved candlestick, and with a flat handle.
2.215

M127 Charity box
silver, engraved
Maker's mark: *A.M.* (Ant. Marouschek 1819–54)
3.5×2.8, 226 gm.
In the form of a circular dish divided in three sections, with a wide rim engraved with a Hebrew inscription and bearing a candlestick, opposite which is a curved handle.
Donor: David, son of Shemuel Kompert, 1824
2.209

BOOK AND SCROLL COVERS

M128 Book cover* (page 1)
silver, filigree
Unmarked
6.2×4.5, 35 gm.
Decorated with leaves and blessing hands, with a clasp. Binding for a Hebrew book of 318 folios, published in Amsterdam 1739.
174.900

M129 Scroll case* (page 152)
silver, gilt and filigree
Unmarked
11.8×3, 101.5 gm.
A cylindrical case of filigree and beading with a handle at one end and containing a scroll of the Book of Esther.
175.804

COMBS AND FILES

M130 Comb and files*
silver
Unmarked
9.6×5.1, 80 gm.
The comb is formed of two sets of teeth with a chased Hebrew inscription on the spine. Three files and case are attached to one side of the comb by a chain, and joined together at the top by a bolt. The case is engraved with decoration including the face of a man.
Donor: Mosche, son of Yitzhak, 1770.
4.520

M131 Comb and files
silver
Maker's mark: *T.R.*; hallmark: Brno, 1835
5.1×10.9, 70 gm.
The comb is engraved along the spine with a Hebrew inscription within a border; two rings join to it four files.
10.344

M132 Comb
silver
Hallmark: Prague, 1806–07
9.7×14.9, 140 gm.
The comb has two curved indentations along the top of the spine and is engraved with Hebrew inscriptions. Three chains are attached to the comb by links through three holes along the upper edge.
37.731

M133 Comb and file
silver
Maker's mark: *A.K.*; hallmark: Bohemia
9.1×13, 115 gm.
Comb with two rows of teeth, the spine with an engraved Hebrew inscription, a single file attached by a ring to one side.
9.860

M134 Comb and file
silver
Maker's mark: *K.S.*; hallmark: Jihlava, 1803
5.5×12.3, 92 gm.
The body of the comb is engraved with a Hebrew inscription within a border, and the bow-shaped edge is pierced with three holes from which spring three chains linked to a spirally fluted file.
Donors: Lipman, son of Asher G"R and Abraham Meir, son of Yehoshua G"S, 1803, Batelov.
37.398

M135 Comb
silver
Maker's mark: *A.K.*; hallmark: Prague, 1929
6×10.2, 50 gm.
The comb has an engraved Hebrew inscription and a chain running through a single central hole at the upper edge.
Donor: Asher, son of Yitzhak Tutčapa, Tutčapy.
54.595

ḤANUKAH LAMPS

M136 Ḥanukah lamp
metal, silvered, repoussé and chased
Maker's mark; Germany (?) end of 19th century
30.2×29.5, 562 gm.
Two lions rampant, rear regardant, at either side support a canopy beneath which appears a peacock. The arched top supports a large crown and is flanked by acanthus foliage, on the right side is a beadle light (candleholder). The whole stands on a rectangular base at the front of which is a low rail with eight candleholders.
121.496

M137 Ḥanukah lamp
brass
Unmarked; c.1860
40.5×22
In the form of a candelabrum. A baluster stem on a domed circular base, with a cast acanthus moulding serving as a knop, from which spring two lyre-shaped arms. These flank a large medallion with an embossed lion's head, below which protrudes a hand grasping the handle of a beadle light (oil burner) and support a bar with eight oil lamps surmounted by a cast Star of David finial.
37.527

M138 Ḥanukah lamp
brass
Maker's mark; c.1850
57×35
In the form of a candelabrum. A baluster stem on a circular domed base supports two lyre-shaped arms and a large ring, surmounted by a bar with eight oil burners. Protruding from the junction of the arms is a hand grasping a beadle light (oil burner).
13.522

M139 Ḥanukah lamp
metal, repoussé
c. end of 18th century
55×23
In the form of a candelabrum. The tapering fluted stem, decorated at its base with repoussé foliage, rests on three claw feet on stand. Springing from open palm leaves at the top of the stem are an oil lamp and ornate branches supporting a bar with eight further lamps.
2.904

M140 Miniature Ḥanukah lamp
brass
2nd half of 19th century
13.2×12.9, 250 gm.
On four legs, the base supports eight candleholders, and behind them a curved bar from which springs the cast outline of a crown containing a lion rampant, surmounted by a beadle light (candleholder).
66.650

M141 Ḥanukah lamp
brass, cast
East Europe, 18th century
12×10.8, 352 gm.
Eight oil burners on feet, behind which spring two lions rampant, rear regardant, supporting a seven-branched candelabrum surmounted by a ring from which the whole lamp is suspended. A beadle light (candleholder) is attached to the right-hand lion.
174.915

M142 Ḥanukah lamp
brass, pierced, chased
East Europe, 18th century
15×23, 725 gm.
Formed as a rack on four legs, with a row of eight oil burners along the bottom edge of a rectangular backplate pierced with round holes. At the centre, four pierced trefoils surround a protruding beadle light (oil burner), above which is a Star of David. The upper edge has a small central arch surmounted with a crown.
174.349

M143 Ḥanukah lamp
brass
French-Italian, 17th – 18th century
13×15.5, 1250 gm.
A rack of eight oil burners supported on four feet, below a pierced backplate surmounted by a ring and a protruding beadle light (candleholder).
32.326

M144 Ḥanukah lamp
brass, pierced and engraved
East Europe
34×36, 4125 gm.
Formed as a rack on four feet, with pierced balustrade front and tray of eight oil burners inside. The side panels, bearing candleholders, below which are bolted cast birds, are in the form of two lions rampant, rear regardant, and support an elaborate pierced architectural backplate from the roof of which springs a pierced tiered ornament of two birds flanking a plant finial.
12.455

M145 Ḥanukah lamp*
brass
East Europe, 18th century
18.8×26.5, 1585 gm.
In the shape of a rack, with tray of eight oil burners at the front, the sides in the form of crowned lions rampant. The backplate is of volute scroll, and in the centre, a medallion encircled by a laurel wreath above which is a Star of David in a crest of palm foliage.
66.649

M146 Ḥanukah lamp
brass
Central Europe, Prague (?), 2nd half of 19th century
18×26.3, 1193 gm.
In the form of a rack with tray of eight oil burners at the front and figurative side panels flanking an ornamental backplate of 'C'-scrolls with embossed flowers, in the centre of which is a medallion encircled by a laurel wreath.
121.157

M147 Ḥanukah lamp
silver-plated
Unmarked; probably 1890
49.5×34.3, 1070 gm.
In the form of a candelabrum, the baluster stem resting on a raised, tiered base and supporting on either side four 'S'-scroll foliage arms with oil burners at the extremities. At the top of the stem is a ninth burner (beadle light) and the whole is surmounted by an eagle finial.
66.664

M148 Ḥanukah lamp
brass
c.1900
23.8×21.5, 375 gm.
In the form of a candelabrum, the short baluster stem on a stepped base supports two radial arms of a segment enclosing a Star of David. From the circumference spring eight arms with oil burners linked by circles pierced with stars, and a ninth burner (beadle light) protrudes from the centre.
66.665

M149 Hanukah lamp
metal, parcel-gilt
Germany, end of 19th century
44.7×30.7, 1180 gm.
In the form of a candelabrum. The double baluster stem rests on a stepped circular base decorated with repoussé foliate scrolls, bearing an engraved German inscription, and supports with scrolls of flowers and foliage a cross-bar mounted with eight candleholders; at the centre an imitation flame. Protruding from the centre is a ninth candleholder (beadle light).
8.266

M150 Hanukah lamp
metal, parcel-gilt, repoussé, chased and engraved
c.1830
30×20.7, 1200 gm.
In the form of a candelabrum, the shaft rests on a stepped and domed base engraved with foliage, with beading around the wave-shaped rim. From the top of the shaft spring bow-shaped foliate arms in the centre of which is a flower with six alternate leaves and petals, which support eight oil lamps, surmounted by a Star of David.
12.805

LAMPS

M151 Sabbath lamp*
brass
1st half of 18th century
34×23, 1900 gm.
The oil burners, in the shape of a six-pointed star, are connected to the ring finial from which the structure is suspended by a baluster shaft, which opens at the top into an inverted bell.
37.006

M152 Sabbath lamp
brass
1st half of 18th century
54.5×29, 5250 gm.
The eight oil burners in the form of a star, beneath which hangs a circular drip bowl, is connected by a baluster shaft to a ring finial

through which passes a ratchet suspension hook, ornamented with a bird.
32.993

M153 Sabbath lamp
brass
c.1880
53×29, 6905 gm.
The eight burners in the form of a star, beneath which hangs a circular drip bowl, which is connected by a baluster shaft to a ring through which passes a large ratchet suspension hook, ornamented with a bird.
173.102

M154 Sabbath lamp
brass
2nd half of 18th century
42×33, 5320 gm.
The ten oil burners in the shape of a star are connected to a baluster stem ornamented at its base with applied rosettes. From a plate serving as a knop spring ornate scrolls, four of which support candleholders in dishes, the remaining four with applied rosettes. The whole is surmounted by a ring from which the structure is suspended.
32.888

CIRCUMCISION SET

M155 Circumcision set
c.1900
Box: 20×9, 150 gm.
The black wooden case contains a rectangular silver dish, a silver knife, a glass bottle, and shield.
12.785, 1-4; bottle: 2.292

MEZUZAH CASES

M156 Mezuzah case
wood
c.1900
20.8×2.4
The case is carved with ornament and with a rectangular opening which reveals a

parchment inscribed with verses from Deuteronomy.
23.926

M157 Mezuzah case
wood
c.1900
16.8×3
The case is carved with lattice ornament and with a Star of David. A circular opening reveals a parchment scroll.
66.492

M158 Mezuzah case
metal
c.1900
8×3
The case has carved ornament and a glass oval front which reveals a parchment scroll.
66.499

M159 Mezuzah case
metal
c.1900
The cylindrical case, containing a parchment scroll, is mounted on a plaque with embossed foliage ornament.
66.510

AMULETS

M160 Amulet
silver, repoussé and chased
end of 19th century
5×4
Two twisted columns flank a Hebrew inscription, above which appears a 'C' scroll and a shell, surmounted by a ring.
4.000

M161 Amulet
silver, repoussé and chased
Of architectural form, ornamented with rosettes and inscribed in Hebrew.
12.788

M162 Amulet
silver
Length: 3
In the form of a hand, the fingers embossed and with Hebrew inscription and hole at the top.
4.525

Burial Brotherhood paintings

Among the oldest paintings in the Museum's collection are those, made about 1773, of the Burial Brotherhood (*Ḥevra Kadisha*). Ceremonies connected with death and burial are depicted in fifteen paintings. The sequence begins with a visit to a sick person and ends with mourners washing their hands after leaving the cemetery. The artist is unknown but he had a strong narrative sense.

The paintings were originally destined for the Burial Brotherhood Assembly Room. Four paintings that were added to the cycle in the mid–nineteenth century depict different scenes in the life of the Brotherhood, including its annual banquet, and members praying at Rabbi Löw's tomb. The original idea of the cycle was probably to display the importance of this association in the social life of the Prague Jewish community.

The same master who executed the Burial Brotherhood cycle also painted eight miniature portraits of members of the Burial Brotherhood in 1773. He emphasises the characteristic features of those who sat for him and this set is the oldest in the Museum's collection of portraits.

P17 Portrait of Lezer Zekeles 1773   P16 Portrait of Isaak Austerlitz 1773

PICTURE CYCLE OF THE PRAGUE BURIAL
BROTHERHOOD
Unknown folk painter c.1780

P1 Visit to the sick man*

oil on canvas: 55×110
The invalid lies in a canopied bed in a room
furnished in the Rococo style. An elderly man
and a woman and child are standing round the
bed whilst a seated physician (possibly Jona
Jeiteles, physician to the Jewish congregation
at that time) is seated holding up a small bottle
of medicine in his left hand.
12.843/1

P2 Prayers at the dead man's bed*

oil on canvas: 55×110
Round the bed of the dead man are gathered
nine old men with beards and black,
three-pointed hats. They are praying and
holding prayer-books and lighted candles.
A weeping woman (possibly the dead man's
widow) leads a child towards a door on the
left. The Venetian mirror, displayed in the first
painting of this cycle, has been replaced by a
chandelier with five branches holding lighted
candles.
12.843/2

**P3 The Brothers taking custody of the
dead man***

oil on canvas: 55×110
The dead man, wrapped in white linen, is
being placed on the floor by four kneeling
members of the Burial Brotherhood. The fifth
kneeling figure binds together his toes. Above
them stand another three old men, one with a
candle in his hands. To the right, another man,
sitting at the table, reads the prayers.
12.843/3

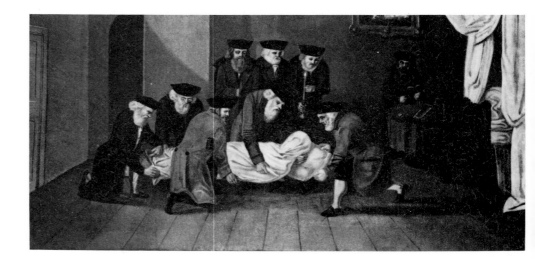

P4 The making of the shroud*

oil on canvas: 55×110

The scene takes place in front of the building of the Burial Brotherhood near the Old Prague Jewish Cemetery. To the left are two men, one of whom is sitting at a table and cutting the cloth for the shroud. To the right, in two bays of the building's walls, sit two seamstresses who are also working on the shroud.

12.843/4

P5 The washing of the body*

oil on canvas: 55×110

In the room of the Burial Brotherhood the dead man's body is laid on a trestle table. It is being washed and prepared for the grave by members of the Burial Brotherhood. In an open doorway, on the right, stands a group of people who are praying and weeping. Various Hebrew inscriptions are hung on the walls of the room.

12.843/5

P6 Carrying the body out of the house*

oil on canvas: 55×110

The body, wrapped in the shroud, is being carried on a board out of the house of the Burial Brotherhood by four men. In the centre of the composition are a weeping man and child, and another man is inserting a coin into a small alms box carried by an old man. To the right stands a group of men waiting with the bier. In the background are a number of brick houses and the wall of the cemetery.

12.843/6

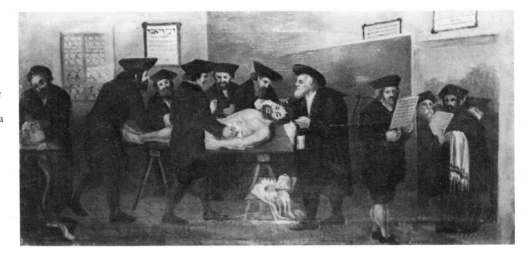

P7 The digging of the grave*
oil on canvas: 55×110
Two men are digging the grave in the Old
Prague Jewish Cemetery. On the left, a third
man is bringing the burial board, and a fourth
man approaches, carrying a hoe over his
shoulder.
12.843/7

**P8 The entrance of the burial procession
into the cemetery***
oil on canvas: 55×110
The procession, headed by men carrying the
body on a burial board, passes under the
archway of a house.
12.843/8

P9 The oration over the dead man*
oil on canvas: 55×110
The officiating rabbi stands on a three–stepped
platform in a bay of a cemetery wall. His arms
are outstretched and he wears a long coat and a
fur cap. The dead man's body, which is
covered with a *tallit* (prayer shawl), lies in
front of him on a stretcher. Members of the
Burial Brotherhood and relatives are grouped
to the right and left.
12.843/9

P10 Carrying the body to the grave*
oil on canvas: 55×110
At the head of the procession eight men carry
the burial board with the corpse. In the middle,
an old man is flanked by two younger men and
the procession concludes with two young men
and an elderly man with the small alms box.
12.843/10

P11 The making of the coffin*
oil on canvas: 55×110
In the cemetery two men cut the wood for the
coffin. Another two men carry the stretcher
along a path to the left. On both sides of the
path are tombstones, partly overgrown with
shrubs.
12.843/11

P12 Lowering the body into the grave*
oil on canvas: 55×110
The open coffin is lowered into the grave by
four men using ropes. Another man stands by
the grave holding the coffin lid. To the left is
an old man with a stick, to the right a weeping
man and boy, behind whom is a group of three
men.
12.843/12

P13 After the burial*

oil on canvas: 55×110

A weeping man and boy sit on the steps in front of the small house with the arched opening in the cemetery. The mourners are confronted by an old man to the left and another two men to the right. The grave-digger with his spade departs to the left, and, at the right edge of the picture, a figure prays at the tombstone.

12.843/13

P14 Washing hands on leaving the cemetery*

oil on canvas: 55×110

In front of the open gate of the cemetery the hands of the mourners are washed at a pump which bears the date *1697* and is operated by a boy.

12.843/14

P15 Group portrait of members of the Prague Burial Brotherhood*

oil on canvas: 55×110

The members are gathered in four small groups in front of the cemetery wall with its bays. To the left are two men with a plaque and a rolled document, a man holding two vessels, and to the right of them a group consisting of Israel Frankl, the Head, Isaak Austerlitz, the First Superior, and Abraham Riss, the Superior. The next group is made up of four men: Lezer Zekeles, the Superior, Leb R. Feivel, the Arbitrator, Pinkas R.M.D., the Superior of the congregation and Arbitrator, and Wolf Bumsla, the Superior of the Alt-Neu Synagogue and Arbitrator of the Burial Brotherhood. On the right are a further two male figures.

12.843/15

P16 Isaak Austerlitz (page 145)
oil on cardboard: 15×11
Wearing a black coat with a wide collar and a
black, three-pointed hat; brown curly wig, a
thin moustache and a short grey beard;
inscription: *Yitzhak Segal Austerlitz, superior of
the congregation and 'gabbai'* (treasurer) *of the
Burial Brotherhood, r. 533 p.m.p.* (1773)
17.820/1

P17 Lezer Zekeles (page 145)
oil on cardboard: 14.5×11
The head half turned to the right and the right
hand inserted under the sitter's coat;
grey-brown coat with a wide black collar and a
black three-pointed hat; brown wig and a grey
beard; inscription: *Lezer Zekeles, 'stadlan'*
(advocate) *and 'gabbai'* (treasurer) *of the Prague
Burial Brotherhood, r. 533 p.m.p.* (1773)
17.820/2

P18 Wolf Bumsla
oil on cardboard: 14.5×11
The head turned a little to the left; brown coat
with a wide black collar and a black
three-pointed hat; brown curly wig and a grey
goatee beard; inscription: *Wolf Bumsla, superior
of the synagogue and member of the board of trustees
of the Burial Brotherhood, 533 p.m.p.* (1773)
17.820/3

P19 Rabbi Leb R. Feivel
oil on cardboard: 14.5×11
The head slightly turned to the left; brown
coat with a black collar and a black oval hat;
grey short hair, moustache and beard;
inscription: *Leb R. Feivel Dayan, member of the
board of trustees of the Burial Brotherhood, r. 533
p.m.p.* (1773).
17.820/4

P20 Jona Jeiteles
oil on cardboard: 14.5×11
The head slightly turned to the right; white
stock, yellow silk waistcoat and black coat;
clean shaven with a short powdered white
wig; inscription: *Jona Jeiteles, sworn physician of
the congregation, r. 533 p.m.p.* (1773).
17.820/5

P21 Israel Frankl
oil on cardboard: 14.5×11
The head slightly turned to the left; brown
coat with a black collar, the lace frill of his shirt
is visible through the opening of his coat; grey
curly wig and a beard, though the rest of his
face is clean-shaven; inscription: *Israel Frankl,
head of the Burial Brotherhood and head of the
congregation, r. 533 p.m.p.* (1773)
17.820/6

P22 Abraham Riss
oil on cardboard: 14.5×11
Wearing a brown coat with a black collar, the
lace frill of his shirt is visible through the
opening of his coat; brown curly wig, narrow
moustache and grey beard; inscription:
*Abraham Riss, superior of the synagogue and
member of the board of trustees of the Burial
Brotherhood, r. 533 p.m.p.* (1773).
17.820/7

P23 Pinkas RMD
oil on cardboard: 14.5×11
The head slightly turned to the left; brown
coat with a black collar and a black
three-pointed hat; brown curly hair and beard,
though the upper lip is clean-shaven;
inscription: *Pinkas R.M.D., superior of the
congregation and member of the board of trustees of
the Burial Brotherhood, r. 533 p.m.p.* (1773).
17.820/8

M129 Scroll case, silver, gilt